The Train From Greenville

The Train From Greenville

a travel story

Anna Raglan

OLD
TREE
PRESS

Printed in the United States of America
Interior formatting by Luminare Press

OLD
TREE
PRESS

Old Tree Press
Front Royal, VA
www.oldtreepress.com

LCCN: 2021913146
ISBN: 978-1-7373926-0-6

In memory of my dear,
funny friend Ann, 1952-2019.
So much there.
She loved the world,
including travel, including books.
She worked to make life better for others,
believed in second chances,
and I like to believe that she is traveling still.

And thank you to the YERT kids,
whose own travel story is a source of never-ending
enjoyment and inspiration for me.
And to my family and friends.
And to Book People.
To everyone, really.

Contents

There needs to be more laughing in the world.

—OVERHEARD ON A TRAIN

Prologue

A long, long time ago, somewhere in spacious Africa, another extraordinary thing happened, and the first humans came into being.

We humans didn't seem to be in any hurry back then, mostly. We stayed in spacious Africa for years and years, many thousands of years, almost forever we might say today, spreading out.

Then someone from the place we now call Ethiopia got a wild case of wanderlust, or some other compulsion, and left home-town Africa for the wilds of the Near East. And so it continued, people spreading out.

An Ice Age happened. Sea water turned into glacial ice. A new land bridge appeared, beckoning wanderers from Asia. Come on over! Try the Americas!

Time passed.

People invented things, as always.

People struggled, people loved.

Ideas came and ideas went.

In the 1830s, in America, Ralph Waldo Emerson hit a dead end, decided he couldn't be a minister after all, wandered over the Atlantic Ocean to France, returned to America, and eventually decided that any religious belief must include a harmony with nature, which was news to the American intellectuals of his day. A few years later, Emerson's friend Thoreau decided that he had been spending too much of his time working for money. Thoreau decided to live more simply.

In the 1950s, a father and son took a train trip across the prairie in North Dakota and Montana. As they rode along, the father told his son stories of their family and the land, and the son felt a beginning of love for it all. Somewhere on the same prairie, a Native American family rode horses, trained horses, understood horses, and told their own stories of family, land and love. These are stories like no other.

Martin Luther King Jr., a devoted minister, wrote this in the sixties: "Darkness cannot drive out darkness, only light can do that."

October, 1999. An Ethiopian woman brought a 15-year-old child of the streets into her home. It was just the beginning.

And on a decidedly more ordinary scale, in July of 2011, a reluctant traveler, as reluctant to travel as the hobbit Bilbo Baggins, left her home in North Carolina to start on an adventure, feeling, as did Bilbo, "a bit shaky inside."

CHAPTER 1

2011: July

We rode in silence.

Dee drove.

My silence was a happy one, welcome, almost giddy. His? I didn't know, or care.

Was his a happy silence? He had a mission. We were lost and he was driving. And it was getting dark. And we were going further and further into the middle of a darkening nowhere. Or maybe we weren't. Maybe just ahead, around the next curve, was the beginning of the somewhere that would take us where we wanted to go.

And time counted for more than just the end of daylight. I had a train to catch. We were trying to find the train station in Greenville, South Carolina, a city of sixty thousand. We had directions, but everything around us was looking very country, and more country by the mile. Deep country. Dark country. We were deep in the woods. Sometimes we'd pass an old dark building, a gas station or a store, long past its prime, closed for the day, or abandoned, it was sometimes hard to tell.

But my silence was happy. Maybe you think I was feeling triumphant, that Dee had been confident about the directions, and now was looking in the wrong.

No. The directions were from me, carefully printed from the internet weeks earlier. At least the first directions were. Search: Amtrak Station Greenville SC.

We were now on the second set of directions, the ones given when we had asked for help. The internet directions were wrong. We had agreed on that, finally, miles and miles ago. They seemed good. They were taking us somewhere promising, somewhere with people, somewhere with houses and businesses. I defended my directions vigorously when Dee began to doubt. We drove many wrong miles on the fuel of my defense. They *were* taking us somewhere, just not, as it turned out, to Greenville.

The dark country road came after I had finally given in and we had agreed, no, my directions were not taking us to Greenville, and yes, we should turn around. We were given new directions from someone we didn't know named Amy, and we had ended up deep in the woods. So far, the Amy directions didn't seem any better than mine.

My internet directions had been good ones, in a sense, maybe even perfect. They were just taking us to the wrong train station. We didn't know this at the time. I found it out much later. They were taking us to the town of Clemson, also in South Carolina, to a station which is, or was, "unstaffed." What would have happened if I, a novice train traveler, prone to worry, had shown up at an unstaffed station, the wrong station, with only a printed itinerary? Ticket purchased, rail pass purchased, but no ticket, no pass.

Well.

It wouldn't have felt smooth.

I had carefully planned a smooth day.

No errands, no calls to make, not a last-minute anything. All day to pack, then leave for the train at six p.m.

I was worried, neurotically worried, crazy worried about this train trip.

I had given myself the full day to pack so that I could have fun packing, or pretend to have fun. I had allotted plenty of time to drive to Greenville, to find the station and scout it out, and plenty of time to leave the station and breathe easy and find a good place for a good dinner. That was going to be the good part. That was going to be the only part that I dared to think would be good. I love to eat. It would be a great dinner. I daydreamed about it.

There were four restaurants near the train station on the map I'd printed out along with the directions from the internet. I'd never used a map from the internet before, and discovered that it came with tiny boxes drawn out and labelled with restaurant names. Restaurant choices! One of my favorite things. Extra incentive for daydreaming! Two fast food places, plus two folksy-sounding restaurants, one Mexican and one a diner. Not the fast food. I wanted a slow and distracting dinner, something special. Sometimes in my daydreams I'd choose the diner and there would be a friendly Southern waitress and mashed potatoes. Sometimes I would chose Mexican. Maybe I'd speak my horrible Spanish to our young waiter, and he would laugh with us. Hahaha, we'd have fun together. What would I order? I thought about enchiladas. I love enchiladas. I thought about how good I am at picking restaurants.

Then one lazy afternoon, two weeks before the trip, the tiny memory of a bad choice interrupted a daydream. The bad choice memory would not go away and, instead, kept growing in size and detail. Here are a few of the details. We are stuck in traffic that is both rush hour and holiday. We have five hours to go to get to a relative's house. We inch past a restaurant billboard featuring a mouth-watering plate of spaghetti. It is dinnertime. I am so hungry and bored. I make my argument. Maybe the traffic will clear up while we eat, I say.

The restaurant is packed. Maybe I'm not the only traveler who had this idea. We wait and wait to give our order. Dee hates to wait in restaurants. I spy a roach along the baseboard, but don't tell Dee about it. Our waitress is really busy, but really nice. Really Southern. She apologizes, when she breezes by, apologizes with remarkable energy, and seems genuinely sorry that she can't get to us just yet. She is young, and she is "up," and she is making life work out by being up, or so it seems. Which is fine. Really. I know that world. It has its place.

Our waitress finally has time to take our order. While we wait for our food, she cheerfully refills my water and Dee's tea, when she can. We wait. At long last, she comes to our table and tells us with an honest and jolly laugh that the cook has not shown up for his shift. She says she is sorry, and I believe her. We decide to leave, not a difficult decision, no discussion needed. Dee puts a tip on the table, and we return to the car in silence. I eat some crackers that I pocketed from the restaurant, and offer him some in a cheerful manner, and he declines tersely. The traffic has not improved.

An unfortunate pick. And, come to think of it, there were others. So the smart thing to do on the day that was supposed to be smooth was to let Dee choose. I was just as happy, as it turned out, because I decided he wouldn't pick fast food. I could still daydream. My daydreams never got to the part where we finished dinner and went back to the train station. Why go there?

When the real day came–the day to start on the trip that I could hardly bear to think about, any thought of which, beyond the pleasant dinner daydreams, beyond the dutiful packing decisions, I would hurriedly and fearfully sweep under the rug of denial–when that day finally came, it started out nicely. This was summer, and the day was pretty. I went about my packing in an easy way because I'd already made most of the decisions. I'd carry three things: a suitcase, a daypack and an open canvas bag. I fetched and arranged, and if I found myself getting tense, I'd quit for a while and goof around or find something to eat.

At 6 p.m., as planned, I slipped my carefully packed daypack over my shoulder, grabbed my packed suitcase in one hand and packed canvas bag in the other, and walked out to the driveway and put them all in the back of Dee's truck. It was 6:15, actually, but that was OK. The sun was warm, the breeze was cool, and my packing was done and done well, I thought. I'd cleared a hurdle. And, anyway, I had built in some cushion for the time schedule. I went back into the house.

"I'm ready," I said to Dee.

"Now?" he said, surprised, looking up from his magazine (*Sports Illustrated*). He knew that it only took two hours to drive to Greenville and that my train didn't leave until eleven.

I nodded.

He did not know my plans for the day, the getting to the station early, the scouting, the temporary escape to the great dinner. He had no idea about the extent of my fears. I just couldn't talk about those things. I didn't completely understand them myself. I wasn't inclined to look at them. But he must have figured I had things on my mind, and he got up cheerfully and we headed to Greenville.

For the first hour of our two-hour drive, I watched the familiar scenery, intensely, and listened intensely to the radio and chatted about anything but the trip. I acted happy. Inside, fear reigned. Fear of the unknown, or fear that we'd never make it to the train station, or that there wasn't really a train station, or existential angst, or whatever it was. I felt like I was going to jail.

I was to be the navigator, and like to navigate, so that much was good. An hour after our start, we exited the familiar road, a road we'd driven a hundred times, and began to follow my internet directions. I'd never been to Greenville. I quit chatting. We drove through country-side, relaxing countryside, and then started working our way into bits and pieces of commerce—used car lots, auto parts stores, gas stations and car washes, tiny strip malls. I started feeling better. We're getting close, I thought. I also thought about the businesses we were passing. What might they say about the current state of humankind? What would a sociologist say, or an anthropologist? Dee broke into my quiet and peaceful wonderings.

"I don't think this is right."

"What do you mean?"

I knew he wasn't commenting on the state of humanity. I felt sick.

"I think we're going away from Greenville."

"Oh, no, I'm sure this is right." I felt desperately unsure. "It's probably a new station and they don't build these things in the city anymore." I spoke quickly. "It's too expensive!" That was a good answer, I thought.

But it was a bluff, and I remained captive to the quiet panic.

"I don't remember this," he said.

Oh.

Oh, that. My panic subsided.

He was wrong. My internet directions were right.

He was thinking about the trip with Ron, his good buddy Ron.

Ron, our neighbor, lived in Chile once, in his younger years. One of Ron's Chilean friends came to visit and arrived by train. I never thought to ask why this friend took the train. I must have thought that the fact he was from Chile explained somehow the reason he traveled by train.

No one I knew, no one we knew, traveled then or travels now by train. No one. I know many travelers. They fly or they drive.

The fact that Ron's friend came in on the train was novel for us, but we all had busy lives. The bigger interest was the practical one, a trip to the unknown station two hours away in Greenville to meet the train that came and left at night. Ron didn't want to go by himself, and had asked Dee along. I had forgotten this.

A car trip at night, years previously, the two of them joking around, Dee not even driving. Completely unreliable information!

I smiled inwardly, not wanting to be rude.

"I'm sure this is right," I repeated.

But we passed no signs for a train station and no signs mentioning Greenville. Only signs announcing the approach of Clemson. Clemson? The seconds ticked by. Every part of me became tense all over again. I gave in. We pulled over.

We each had a flip phone, and we had a Rand-McNally atlas of state maps. I called Information, got the number for the Amtrak station in Greenville, and called that. While I waited, I found South Carolina in the book of maps. Why wouldn't anyone answer and where in Greenville was the station and who could read the Greenville map insert without a magnifying glass which we didn't have and where were we? Dee called anybody we could think of who might be in front of a computer. No one was. I gave up on the station (which, as it turns out, wasn't open yet) and called Information for the Amtrak 800 number. I tried to be calm, and eventually got Amy at Amtrak, who had never heard of Greenville, SC, but searched and found some kind of directions. She was nice. Good luck, she said.

We back-tracked miles to some tiny-town intersection that Dee figured was the place we could merge the two sets of directions, my old internet ones and the new Amy ones, and we chose another road. Dee chose, really. I was starting to lose interest. It was fun not caring. By the time we had driven miles down that road he chose, which was the country road where I started my story, and the summer darkness was coming on, I didn't care at all. All my worry and all my work to be calm finally cracked, and happiness flooded in. I'd given it my best. I was no longer thinking of Greenville. I was thinking of Charlotte.

We could find Charlotte. I knew that, and confidence is such fun. Charlotte, North Carolina. We'd head north. We wouldn't even need a map. Anyone in the world could figure that out. If you were in South Carolina and wanted to go to North Carolina, you would head north. You would pick roads that had "North" on their highway signs. We could have a good time finding Charlotte!

Charlotte is the regional hub for air traffic. There would be signs. Signs for Charlotte, airport signs, parking signs. There would be people in the airport to help us, day or night. I knew the Charlotte airport.

My aim was Seattle. I wanted to end up in Seattle, across the country. Charlotte could get me there, and I didn't care when. The cost of a plane ticket? I'd worry about that later. Spending the night in the airport? Adventuresome.

Where were we now? It no longer mattered, to me at least.

CHAPTER 2

This Way To Greenville

Dee stayed in the game. While my mind was on Charlotte, he decided that the dark country road was another wrong road. He turned the truck around and re-drove the miles to the intersection that he still thought was the way to join the two sets of directions, and chose another road out. Minutes later we were at the edge of a city, apparently Greenville. I was a little surprised. I had stopped believing.

So I was planning to cross the country by train.

East Coast to West, three thousand miles, days of travel.

Would it be three days or four? It was either three or four, and I avoided further precision. It wasn't necessarily a simple answer. How one counts a half day is arbitrary and time zones take thought. I hated thinking about anything but what to pack. And I didn't care. I didn't care when I got to Seattle. I hardly believed in Seattle. What was the difference, really, between three or four days? I had no control anyway. Through the black unknown that was this venture, I thought I would probably live, and that slender bit of faith was sufficient. What it would actually be like, I didn't even want to consider. It could easily, I thought, be awful.

Why was I going by train? I'll be getting to that. It might not be all that interesting.

In my daypack I had four packages of "good" trail mix, by a "premium" brand, the best available at my modest grocery store, a splurge in my reckoning, because if I ever needed trail mix previously I made my own, in the cheapest, most carbohydrate-laden way I could, using store-brand Cheerios and Chex, bite-sized pretzels, some peanuts and some raisons, little that would excite anyone but me. The "premium" mixes I bought were four different varieties, 6 oz. each, one for each day, allowing generously for four days, in case I couldn't find food along the way across the United States. I splurged on store-bought trail mix as a way of bringing cheer to myself. I also had three apples. I debated about the apples. They are relatively big and heavy, taking up precious space and weight for such a long trip. But, I figured, I could take a long, long time to eat them. There was going to be a lot of time on this trip.

We entered Greenville through what looked like an older section, pleasantly haphazard. I enjoyed the view. Here in Greenville, at last, a little excitement started brewing. I looked into the other cars. Young people were out, two or three to a car. Oh, yes, I remembered. This was Saturday night.

So far so good for Amy's directions, which told us to make a right turn onto Stone Avenue. I began to take an interest in navigation again, looking for Stone Avenue. I read street signs and searched for railroad station signs. After a while Dee figured somehow that we must have overshot the turn and he pulled off into a McDonald's, turned around once more and we then found Stone, a small street which took us from the busy road we were on into a small neighborhood. Could this be right?

I was looking for stateliness. In my life I had been to five American train stations. One was a Long Island station, basically utilitarian. From there I rode the train to Penn Station in New York City, basically utilitarian. At seventeen I took a class trip to Miami on the train. I have no memory of the Miami station. What was in my mind as we searched were the classically beautiful marble stations in Richmond, Virginia and Washington, DC, the beginning and end points for another class trip in my impressionable early school days.

I was thinking of "big" and "marble" as I searched. I didn't expect marble in Greenville. I did expect stateliness. The neighborhood we were driving through was pleasant, but the houses were small and pleasant, not stately. And it was a neighborhood. The businesses were behind us. Familiar doubt rose again. And then, out of the darkness, a tall chain-link fence announced the end of the houses, and Dee pulled through the opened gate and there we were, in the large, long, fence-enclosed lot. If there was a sign for Amtrak, I didn't see it.

We parked, and I stepped down from the truck. I was too excited to speak. There are times when even asphalt can be reassuring. I was more than reassured. For some reason, I was suddenly about to burst with excitement.

Dee started to get my bags out of the back. Not yet, I said. I wanted to scout first. We headed down the long parking lot toward the one building. I'm guessing now that it housed a freight business primarily. It was quietly dignified. The left-hand corner was the glassed Amtrak office and waiting room, lit for the nighttime. Who cares for stateliness, I might have thought. But I didn't. My thinking was more like that of an over-excited eighth grader about to ride a train for the first time. I could have giggled. Dee was smiling. We'd made it.

I was surprised that the waiting room was so small, but became an instant, loyal fan. Plastic bucket seats lined the sides, bolted in evenly spaced fashion to their shiny metal support. Just right. Cheery even. Like the lighting was cheery. The room was clean. It was "of the people." A few travelers with their suitcases and bags were sitting or standing, waiting. It was a quietly friendly place. These were my people, my fellow travelers, and they looked nice. They smiled at me, and I smiled back.

The one employee stood at a counter behind a glass partition, at work on her computer. I felt shy and told myself not to act silly, because it seemed to me I was playing a game. I put my three-page, tri-folded itinerary into the counter depression that connected us. She looked over and pulled it out, unfolded it and read, typed something into her computer, and frowned. My stomach turned.

She looked up. "Do you have a ticket?"

"No, I don't. But I have a reservation." I was stuttering. "And it's paid for."

My printed itinerary, it seemed, did not match the one in her system.

I'd forgotten. There had been a change made in my original route. I'd been contacted by Amtrak weeks after I'd made my reservation. I'd been asked to work out a different route because a trestle somewhere was out. A trestle was out? My mind went to the Wild West while I discussed a second route with the Amtrak phone representative. I wanted to ask for details about that trestle, but decided not to. I didn't want to be a problem for the phone representative. I think she was new. She had to put me on hold twice, I'm guessing to ask her supervisor what to do. She was acting haughty, I'm guessing to cover up some insecurity. I chose another route, but didn't print out the revised itinerary.

Panic was rising again. My itinerary did not match the one in the system. But this wasn't much of a problem, or it didn't seem so for the lovely Amtrak woman, who went about her work quietly and calmly. She immediately became my favorite person, replacing Dee. She worked up my rail pass and a book of tickets for my different trains, put them in an Amtrak envelope, and sent them through the counter tunnel.

I took the envelope and wedged it deep into my pocketbook. I will not lose this, I said to myself. I will not lose this. I gave the Amtrak woman my best thanks, then turned away and my eye caught a sign posted strategically between the ticket counter and the door. The sign gave us passengers the rules about luggage. Below it was a scale.

I wondered and worried what my suitcase weighed, but I passed over that concern to a more troubling bit of information. One suitcase and one carry-on, not counting pocketbook or computer, the sign said. One carry-on?

Dee had been wandering around and came up then, and I grabbed his sleeve. "Look at that," I whispered. He studied the sign. I read it again. We looked at each other, and I nodded towards the door. It would be my last act of leadership for a long time.

At the truck, Dee dropped the tailgate and dumped out the contents of the two carry-ons, my daypack and my open canvas bag. All my good work. The packing had been a source of comfort, something I could control, something to do, a harmless place for neurotic indulgence, a way to avoid my jitters. My reason for existence had been simplified—what would I choose to put into the open bag, to reach easily? What into each pocket of the pack? All this was dumped onto the tailgate. Dee seemed happy to have a purpose again and worked with confidence while I could only watch weakly, laughing from time to time in a helplessly lunatic kind of way. My reserves were ebbing.

The suitcase was left alone. It was for my ten days in Seattle and judged by Dee to be well within the weight restriction.

Fine, I said.

"You should take the daypack," he said.

Fine.

He stuffed.

First in was my feather pillow, an extravagance, brought because I was afraid of not sleeping at all on these days and nights of travel, brought, if not to help me sleep, then to be a sort of companion. Being feather, and small, it stuffed beautifully. Nothing else was as accommodating. But there was nothing I wanted to leave behind. Two books, knitting, a notebook and pens, plastic sandals, a blanket, a headlamp, the food, a water bottle, a minimum of clothing changes, a bathroom bag, a Ziploc bag with a washcloth, a cotton cardigan, a cheap pair of eye shades, and a cheap U-shaped neck pillow filled with buckwheat hulls and conspicuously displaying the name "Wild River."™ Dee shoved it all.

My daypack was an odd one, made of black mesh. Dee wedged in the final item, the bathroom bag, then slowly worked the zipper closed over it, over the little bathroom bag with the blue Hawaiian design that is one of my favorite possessions, and proudly held up his work. I covered my eyes, leaned against the truck, and laughed. The mesh had done its mesh thing. My pack was a butterball. I was going to be the weird traveler.

We had some time, not much, before the train left. Dee suggested a quick dinner at the McDonald's where we'd made the final turnaround. Fine, I said. The McDonald's was full, but in the good way, not in the stressful way, and there was only one person ahead of us in line.

The one person ahead of us was a young man dressed in what I would call "gangster style." He was tall and fit, and as much as I don't want to say this, I felt uneasy when I saw him. Here was what turned out to be the last trial of the day—uneasiness. I saw a young fit man who was dressed in a style unfamiliar to me, in clothes that suggested violence, and even though common sense tried to tell me that there was not going to be any violence, I still felt uneasy. Being female was part of my anxiety, unfamiliarity was part of it. Where I lived, in the country, stylish and fit young men often wore camo, and if that doesn't suggest violence to the uninitiated, what would? But I was used to camo, didn't give it a thought, and often had tender feelings towards the wearer, not because of his clothes, not in spite of his clothes, but because he was young and he was in this world, which is often tough.

The cashier, a middle-aged woman, asked the young man for his order and he listed the things he wanted. She repeated each item as she keyed, doing what she

Anna Raglan

was certainly trained to do. At every repeat he answered, "Yes, ma'am." Surprise. Yes, ma'am. Big surprise. A gentleman. A sweet guy. I was witness to a courtly call-and-response. Welcome to blessed Greenville.

Dee was reading the menu high on the wall behind the counter. "Do you know what you want?" he asked.

"I don't want anything."

He turned to look at me. Dee, too, loves to eat.

"Nothing?"

I shook my head.

"I've lost my appetite."

He stared. "Something to drink?"

"No. I don't think so."

He stared a second more, then turned back to order.

Dee ate his dinner in silence, content, and I watched people. It was enormously pleasant to be quiet and to be looking in on other lives, not having to live my own. I hadn't felt this relaxed all day. Saturday night, out at McDonald's, in a new city, everybody seemed happy. This is all right, I thought. This is nice.

CHAPTER 3

The Train

Just outside the Greenville Amtrak office and waiting room, to the left as you looked at the office building from the long parking lot, was a cement platform, triangle-shaped, open and airy, a well-delivered stone's throw away from, and slightly above, the empty train track. We were there on a lovely summer evening. The platform could have been a patio, and we who waited for the train the relaxed party-goers, enjoying ourselves with each other but not overly motivated to make conversation or connections, gazing at the river of track from time to time. At eleven o'clock we were a small crowd of twenty or so, collected into little groups.

"I've always wanted to run alongside a train," Dee said to me. "Like they do in the movies."

What did he say? I barely heard him. My mind was crowded. I was excited, I was nervous. I was also watching the Amtrak woman. She had left her counter and was out with us doing some task, something with the luggage. I was interested in her uniform and in her carefully styled hair that still looked natural. I didn't style my hair in those days. For the trip I had it in a braid. I liked her calm and competent manner. I would have rated her "excellent in her job." She was the first Amtrak employee I'd ever seen. So she was in my mind. I was also wondering if it would be worth my while to make my way to the head of the group when the time for boarding came, so that I could get a good seat. What was a good seat? I wondered. Then I heard the train. "Here it is!" I said to Dee, and to everyone, really, because I was louder than I needed to be.

I shouldered my round backpack with some difficulty, wriggling my arm into the tight space under one of the straps, and then maneuvered my roller suitcase hurriedly and clumsily over to the edge of the platform. Dee moved with me. Would I need to show my ticket? I wriggled out of the backpack and let it fall to the ground to get at my pocketbook. The other travelers were gathering around me.

"It's a freight train," said Dee.

What did he say? I didn't get what he said. Where was my ticket?

"It's the freight train," announced the Amtrak woman to us all. "Your train will be here in seven minutes."

The little crowd fell back to their previous spots, and I stared at the woman, frozen, my hand in my pocketbook. Seven minutes, I thought. That is a long time. How did Dee know it was a freight train? How did she know seven minutes? She explained to someone that our train was running so-and-so minutes late and had just passed through so-and-so, naming a town. I didn't care about the particulars, but all this communication impressed me, and I thought her particularly sharp.

The seven long minutes passed, my mind still full, and we heard the sound of another train coming, and then saw it. I watched in a state of wonder as it pulled in and stopped, then I suddenly snapped to. I gave Dee a hurried kiss and a hurried "Bye!" and left the platform and walked towards the entrance to the car where everyone else was headed. A uniformed man stepped down from the train and sang out, "All aboard!" I grinned. Wow! They still say "All aboard!"

A uniformed woman followed him, and they stood on either side of the entrance to the car. The woman handed out slips of paper, seat assignments it turned out, and as I neared I saw a yellow stepstool on the ground and then a short set of stairs inside the train itself. How could I manage those with my bags? I reached for my seat assignment and started to say something, but the man took my suitcase without a word and swung it up to the floor of the train and I climbed up after it, grabbed the handle, made the left turn towards the open door, and entered the car, my new room of a world.

My seat was near the door. I heaved my suitcase into the overhead and took the window seat I'd been assigned. It was wide and comfortable, the window huge. This was all a beautiful dream.

"But I'm blind," said a worried voice from the direction of the door.

"You'll be alright, honey," was the slightly amused reply, and I saw two women, one behind the other, heading my way. "Right here, honey," said the one behind, the seat assignment person, and the woman in front, with her many things, worked her way into the seat beside me.

Just then the train started moving, and I suddenly remembered what Dee had said about running alongside the train. I leaned forward to look past my new seatmate to the window opposite, the station side. But what I could see was not much, and we were also moving, and it was dark outside. I gave half-second's thought to apologizing and scrambling over my seatmate to get a better look. For a moment, all I wanted in the world was to see him. But, oh well. I sighed. I sat back. I do love Dee. It probably wouldn't work, I thought, trying to catch a glimpse of him. He probably didn't run anyway, I thought. He had a terrible knee back then.

So I settled. All done! We were going along now. There was a gentle side-to-side rocking and a soft clacking rail noise. The whistle sounded at a muffled distance. Otherwise, quiet. Beautiful. Almost unreal.

The inside lights were dim. Outside, darkness. Occasional lights came and went, came and went. I watched the window, hypnotized.

My neighbor, not totally blind apparently, watched something on her laptop. She had pulled her food tray down first thing and set up. I had looked at her when she sat down, but she hadn't looked at me. Maybe I wasn't visible. So we hadn't acknowledged each other. She had other devices in addition to the laptop, as I saw out of the corner of my eye. I didn't know what they were. She had lots of cords and, lovely for me, earphones.

She also had what looked to be the perfect blanket. She'd spread it out right after setting up her screen. Her blanket looked brand new, spotless and pill-less, green maybe. It was hard to identify the color in the dim light. I could see enough, though, to know that it was thin. It had settled and draped so easily over her lap and legs. I suspected it to be an official Amtrak blanket. It was that perfect. I turned back to the window and to the calmness of watching the outside.

After a while I leaned down and zipped open the biggest section of my big round backpack, on the floor at my feet. I found my own blanket, buried. I had been told to bring a blanket. I had labelled myself a clever traveler for bringing a blanket, and had been confident I had the perfect one. I pulled it out carefully, like a magician pulls out the thin silk scarf from his hat. Maybe he pulls it carefully so that he doesn't dislodge and scatter the other stuff he has in his hat. That was my motivation.

My blanket blossomed. It was way too thick. I knew that now. I had thought it was perfect because it was so lightweight. It was certainly the lightest of my blankets, most of them being wool, inherited from my mother, in increments, at each of her down-sizings. I also had thought that my chosen blanket was stylish. I'd bought it years before, at the beginning of the fleece blanket era. It was a name-brand blanket with a plaid design. It had been an extravagance at the time, and I had always been a little proud of it, secretly.

But comparison ever disrupts us. It was too thick, and I could see now what the years had done. They had given it pills and dowdiness. Oh, well. I wasn't going to care. I had a window seat.

I pulled out my pillow next. The train attendant came by handing out little train pillows, and I took one of those, too. I made my nest and watched the night. Our whistle would blow before road crossings, sounding far-away sweet and lovely, and sometimes the crossing would be a town street and we'd travel a moment through the still and lighted scene of a quiet corner. Every so often we'd stop at a sleepy station and I might see a person or two outside. And then underway again, and the gentle rocking, and the dark. It couldn't have been any better.

Two hours went by.

I wasn't letting myself check the time very often. I didn't want to take any steps in the direction of restlessness. Sometimes I'd close my eyes. At 1 a.m. my seatmate disconnected cords and put things away. When I next looked at my phone it was 2 a.m. I'd slept! It seemed a miracle. And so the night went…watching and cat-napping, feeling successful and happy.

Around six o'clock, the world outside began to lighten. I watched the dawning from my comfortable chair, through my huge window.

There's the advantage of having a limited number of things to do. You can witness the gradual lightening of the day. It's an elemental experience for us humans. I don't know if it's true, but I read once that on the moon a day comes in quickly, more like the turning on of a light bulb, because there is so little atmosphere. Lovely earth.

CHAPTER 4

Up And Down

Happiness is a great topic, sometimes a scary one. In one particularly dark period of my life, walled off with a sad and lonely envy of those I deemed happy, I followed many mistakes in my thinking. Thomas Jefferson pondered the subject of happiness. He wrote a lot about happiness. Like most of us, probably every one of us, he couldn't always see the forest for the trees, but his thoughts took some beautiful paths. He took John Locke's excellent "life, liberty, and property," so radical at the time, turned "property" into "the pursuit of happiness," and then gave those words to us, to the world, in his list of some of those things that are rightfully ours. Beautiful. Thanks to him and to all who helped him get to those words.

C. P. Snow, English scientist and novelist, begs to differ. "The pursuit of happiness is a most ridiculous phrase; if you pursue happiness you'll never find it."

I see what he means. Maybe there's truth in both.

Happiness, to me, now, seems more about letting go of the blocks to love, rather than pursuing any particular thing. Letting go of the blocks requires patience and forgiveness, both of which can be practiced. Pursued, in a way.

That's what the teachers say. Happiness first, and all else follows, some say. I'm a beginner. Willing, resistant, forgetful, inconsistent. But teachers are everywhere. Plenty of teachers. Too many to count, really.

Too many to count. Is there anything funny about counting?

Yes, from Lewis Carroll in *Through the Looking-Glass.*

"'Can you do Addition?' the White Queen asked. 'What's one and one and one and one and one and one and one and one and one and one?'

'I don't know,' said Alice. 'I lost count.'

'She ca'n't do Addition,' the Red Queen interrupted."

I was completely happy in those first hours of my time on the train. The happiness wasn't to last, as you will see, but it was a perfect beginning.

In the morning I started feeling hungry. I rummaged blindly in my pack until I felt the four trail mixes, and pulled one out. They were four different mixes, each with a friendly name. The one I got was "Appalachian." It was the one I was secretly wanting to get. I live in Appalachia.

I tore open a corner and poured out a little handful and ate it slowly, single bit by single bit. I was watching

Virginia now, the countryside. The train's route was mostly through woods, with an occasional pasture, looking scruffy, maybe because this was hot July. A scruffy pasture looks beautiful to me. I like the natural look. I love a field or pasture. I ate little handful after little handful, one piece at a time, of endless good trail mix.

A little boy across the aisle and one row up, traveling with his grandmother, realized that he was missing Sunday School, and was disappointed. The man behind me reminisced to his seatmate about traveling on the train when he was a boy. "We carried a shoebox. Everything you needed was in that shoebox." It's easy to hear conversations in a train car because most people are silent.

I thought a bit about national politics and the fight going on in Congress over the budget. Some wanted to hold out, to refuse to agree to a budget they hated. This would, apparently, stop the government. Or some of it. Would my publicly-owned train going west just stop? Would we passengers spill out and start a new story? Tuesday would be the deadline day. I would be somewhere in the far West when Tuesday ended. Things had to be settled by Tuesday, or checks from the government would... well, it depended on who was commenting.

Mid-morning, an announcement was made that the next station would be a "smoke stop," or something like that. I had trouble understanding the intercom. When we did stop, a few people got up. Not many. I sat for several minutes, thinking I should try it but not wanting to risk losing the safety and comfort I'd found. Getting off the train seemed scary. Finally, I made myself get up, excused myself over my seatmate, and went through the door into the vestibule, then took the steps inside the train that led down to the platform. A uniformed man was standing on the platform, facing the steps.

"Are you a smoker?" he asked.

"Oh, no," I said. "I don't smoke."

His face, serious, cracked a bare hint of a smile, as if he couldn't help it. He waved me to my right, alongside the car. "You go down there with the smokers." I walked along the platform to the far end of the car towards the relaxed-looking group of eight or so who were standing around, smoking. This was their good time. Some were quietly smoking. Some were talking and joking in an easy way. These smiled and were friendly to me, and I joined them. We talked about nothing much, just banter. I remember this group well, three years later as I write, though I was with them only a minute or two. I had taken up most of the stop with my indecision. I remember one of the group in particular, one of the friendly ones. He was tall and lanky, about forty, and his face looked kind and intelligent. He didn't run too hard from the tough side of his story and he didn't wallow in it either. That's what you could read on his face. Kindness, good times, and some troubles. You'd bet money he'd be a good friend, trustworthy and easy to talk to, which is the best kind of friend.

"All aboard!" sounded out, we all got back on at the rear entrance to the car, and I found my seat again without much trouble. I counted that as an accomplishment. The excitements of trail mix and the smoke stop filled me for a long time as we rolled along in Virginia on that peaceful Sunday morning.

I used to be a smoker, not much of one. Several of my favorite friends are smokers. I smoked my second year in college, years and years ago. I probably averaged two cigarettes a day. Some people wouldn't even call that smoking.

That second year of college was a restless one for me, restless in a mild way maybe, in a two-cigarette-a-day way. I had no life plan and getting one never crossed my mind. Once I had the plan to transfer to another school and went so far as to apply for the transfer. I never responded to the waiting list letter that I received. I lounged a lot that year, drank a little too much. I felt and exercised a relatively mild wanderlust, an East Coast wanderlust. It was not hard to go places in college. Someone was always going somewhere, so you could catch rides. I was in college in Virginia and caught rides to other schools some weekends, thinking, or hoping I suppose, that the real life was happening elsewhere. Over Christmas break I went to Montreal with some friends, in spring to New Orleans for Mardi Gras. There were certainly good times. But something was lacking. When I look back, I see the lost someone. There was trouble and confusion in the background, and more ahead, the same old story. But help, too. Things worked out, more or less. I did some growing up. One foot in front of the other.

The smoking that year was fun, a communal ritual. I lived in a grand old dorm in the woods at the top of a hill on the corner of campus. Our hall had a central lounge area, invitingly roomy, with windows looking out at the woods, and a big round table in the center. An assortment of us got into the habit of gathering around the table in the afternoon, and someone would pull out a pack of Salems and offer it up. None of us ever talked about the smoking. We just did it. I sensed when it was time to buy a pack, and figured out where on campus the cigarette machines were, taught myself how to use them, with their peculiar clunky lever, and would lay my contribution onto the lounge table nonchalantly, as everyone did. We practiced nonchalance. At least I did. It felt grand.

Part of me would love to be a smoker now. I think about cigarettes sometimes, say, when I'm having a rough time writing, when I'm slogging through the doubt, when the cloud of self-loathing comes rolling in. Wouldn't it be the thing to pull out a cigarette and light it so coolly while staring slit-eyed at that cloud, blow smoke in its face? It seems the very thing. But I have a lousy throat already, for one.

By 2011, the year of the train trip, I had long previously smoked my last cigarette and had also lost every bit of my wanderlust. Every bit. I did not really want to go to Seattle. Adventure to me was reading a good book or taking a walk in the weather of the day or being with a funny friend or trying to learn to play the guitar or going somewhere in the forty-five-minute range from home. There's a lot to be found forty-five minutes from home. Other than that, I was happy with routine. That was my view in 2011.

My adventurous friend Nina did not share my view. She had moved to Seattle two years earlier, making the not uncommon East Coast to West Coast jump, and wanted me to visit. I love Nina. She is very funny, and fun to be with. I would have loved to be in Seattle, magically and instantly. If that wasn't going to happen, I'd be content to wait for her to visit the East. But she kept asking me to come, good friend that she is, and I ran out of delaying excuses. I never told her that I didn't like to travel. It was too embarrassing. I don't think Nina would believe that anyone could really be a homebody.

She didn't believe that I really wanted to take the train. She was definitely right on that one. "Why don't you fly?" she said. "You could have all those extra days here!" I said she'd get sick of me. She said she wouldn't, and I changed the subject. I didn't like talking about the train.

I didn't like thinking about making a reservation either. I didn't know much about trains, didn't know much about computers. I didn't have a computer. But I wanted to make the reservation by computer because I didn't want to talk to anyone.

My friend Francie had a computer and said she'd be happy to help me with a train reservation, and I said I'd take her out to dinner.

We fixed a date and I drove to her house after work. Francie lived forty-five minutes from me in a small town, in a sweet old house on the edge of the tiny downtown. It was mid-June, a just right summertime evening, and we took a long, meandering walk to the downtown street and ate at an outdoor café. I was very chatty. We didn't hurry. We drank some wine. We talked to our waiter and talked to a co-worker of Francie's who came in after us and sat at a neighboring table. I invited him to join us but he had some reports he had to read during dinner. And Francie and I talked to each other, of course. I was full of chattiness, powered with that ready energy of avoidance. By the time we got back to her house, it was getting dark and what I really wanted to do was call it quits and go home.

"We'll have to sit on my bed," Francie said apologetically. "The wireless hasn't been working, and the cable's in my bedroom."

"Oh, fine," I said, secretly thrilled. A bed sounded comforting. I wanted to crawl under the covers.

She opened her laptop, then clicked and typed and scrolled and said "hmmm…" while I breathed and answered a pertinent question or two, such as "When do you want to go?"

Nina had recommended July or August, "Seattle's best weather." You are pretty much guaranteed sun, she said. I had vacation saved and had found three weeks at the end of July and into August that would work. One week of travel out and recovery from travel, one week visit in Seattle, one week travel back and recovery from travel.

From the Amtrak site, Francie was able to verify what I had gathered, that Greenville was the closest passenger train terminal. She plugged in dates and got some routes and fares. I didn't look over her shoulder because I didn't want to crowd her. I sat at a natural and comfortable distance and thought about lying down and curling into a ball and groaning. Groaning would make this more fun, I thought. For me at least.

Then she said something that pulled me into the land of full participation. "It says something here about a rail pass. That might be the cheapest."

A rail pass? Suddenly I was back in college again. The coolest and most romantic thing in the world to me then was "the Eurail Pass." For a multitude of reasons, chiefly fear and lack of money, traveling around Europe on a Eurail Pass was completely out of reach. I knew only the vaguest details about traveling that way, but it seemed the epitome of adventure.

The romance held. My ears picked up. My adventurous side awoke. Maybe I could have a rail pass…

Just as quickly I crashed. "I think I'll call this number," said Francie.

No! No! Not that! I wanted to call an immediate halt to all of this. Wait a minute! Stop! No! We'll be here forever, we'll be on hold forever, we'll get wrong information, it's getting late, we'll get rude people...

I panicked and panicked, in silence. She punched the number. I wanted to go home. She said hello. I wanted to run away, and then we met Thomas.

CHAPTER 5

Amtrak Friend, Amtrak Poetry

Thomas, the Amtrak employee we reached in short order, was a cheerful person and settled in quickly to Francie's questions. Francie pretended to be me and held her phone so that I could hear.

His cheerfulness was not the hyped-up kind. It was natural and easy and therefore calming. It was born, I think, from a boyish personality and a feeling of responsibility for his job, but also from conviction. The conviction was in regard to passenger trains and specifically, of course, Amtrak. Train travel could be fun, and would be fun if you did it right. He was the man of the hour. I pictured him relaxed, with his feet on his desk.

Getting to Seattle was a fairly simple matter with two steps.

Step One: Go through the relatively populous East to railroad central, Chicago.

Step Two: Take the *Empire Builder* from Chicago and cross the vast West all the way to Seattle.

For the route to Chicago there was a choice. Thomas suggested that I get there one way and come back another. I nodded. Francie said, "That sounds good."

"OK!" he said. "Going out we'll take you to Washington, DC, the nation's capital, and going back you'll go through West Virginia. Because you do not want to miss West Virginia."

"Why?" I whispered to Francie. I thought West Virginia sounded lovely, but I wanted to hear his thoughts.

"Why?" asked Francie.

"The trees!" he said. "You want to see the trees!"

"Alright!" she answered. She was in.

She brought up the rail pass idea, and Thomas agreed enthusiastically. I imagine he was happy to have a customer as willing and knowledgeable as Francie. He explained the ins and outs of rail passes.

"Ask him if the seats are comfortable," I whispered.

Oh, goodness, were those seats comfortable! Wide, with armrests, legroom, and—would you believe it—footrests. "Have you heard about the footrests?"

I (we) hadn't.

"Bring a blanket," he said, I guess because we were on the subject of comfort. "Don't forget a blanket because you'll want one." He said they were sold on the train, if I forgot.

"Will it be boring?" I whispered. Thomas was the crystal ball, the Magic Eight Ball. He knew everything.

"Will it be boring?" Francie tried not to laugh.

Well, no, of course it wouldn't be boring. Not to

someone like Thomas. "You don't stay in your seat!" he said, as if that were the biggest mistake made by rail passengers and he appreciated the chance to be a brother and tell me (her).

Where do you go? You go to the Dining Car, the bar, the Observation Car. "You move around."

You move around. Maybe I would have figured that out, but it would have been later rather than sooner, and I don't know if I would have put the words to it. They are useful words in general, aren't they? Sometimes it's the thing to do.

Thomas turned out to be more than man of the hour. He was a guide, one of many to come. His enthusiastic help went a long way that night to dispel at least some of my crazy anxiety. He still makes me smile.

He set up an account and a route for me that night, and locked in the rates for a period of time, a month I think. I liked that. No pressure. Two weeks later I bought dinner for Francie again, and she helped me buy the pass and secure my seat, and then printed out the itinerary.

Maybe you noticed that Thomas told me about the Dining Car. "She knew about the Dining Car!" you might have said, if you read and remembered the part where I said I was bringing trail mix "in case I couldn't find anything to eat along the way."

True. I knew. But I didn't really believe in it. The human mind is great at that sort of thing. Not willing to trust, I had blocked the thought of the Dining Car. For one, a dining car sounded so nostalgically great to someone who loves to eat that it might be too good to be true. And what if there were some mistake made on just my train? What if someone forgot to hitch that car? Oops. And what if my money were stolen? What if I thought the food was too expensive, or I was too uneasy to go? No, my decision of doubt was made, and the whole matter was filed and forgotten. "Fact": there is no Dining Car. Besides, there was a tiny but potent allure to the trail mix. Part of me, a tiny part admittedly, delighted in the thought of adventure, and wanted the test of endurance.

The itinerary that Francie printed was three pages. It listed the trains out and the trains back, and underneath each train, the times of departure and arrival. I glanced at it when it came from the printer, then pressed it into a tri-fold, and that's the way it stayed until the day I left, mostly. I cleared an ample bit of space on the left-hand side of my cluttered dresser, specifically and only for the itinerary. It could not be misplaced.

It had a particular status, a powerful one, a semi-religious one, mixing beauty and fear, trust and doubt, for the month or so that it sat alone in its space. I glanced at it in passing and could see it clearly from where I sat in bed at night to read. With one exception, I found no reason to unfold it. I knew the date of departure and the approximate time: 11 p.m. I told Nina right away the date and time of my arrival into Seattle, and then I promptly erased those details from my memory.

I did love learning that Amtrak named its trains. Here was poetry lending a hand. The best name was the *Crescent*, the New Orleans to New York train. That was the one I would catch first. I would pick it up in the middle of its run and also get off before the New York end. At first I thought that it must have been named for the shape of the route, curving east and north from Louisiana to reach the Atlantic coast above DC. Later, I remembered that New Orleans was nicknamed the Crescent City, maybe because it has that shape too. Either way, "crescent" is a lovely word as well as a lovely shape. There are not many things as pretty as a crescent moon. Who would have thought that something as massive and rocky and scarred as the moon, beautiful in and of itself in a grand way, could also be something as ethereal as an early crescent moon?

I liked the name *Cardinal*, the name of a train I had chosen to take on the return trip. It goes from Chicago to Charlottesville, Virginia, cutting through West Virginia and its wonderful trees. Thomas might have named it something different, after a tree. That was the train I had to cancel, though, the part of the route that had to be changed because of the trestle.

The *Empire Builder* is the name of the train from Chicago to Seattle. I'd heard of it before, on Garrison Keillor's radio show from Minnesota, but didn't know its route and had never thought much about the name. Now I did. Why would anyone name a train "Empire Builder"? It seemed an embarrassing concept to celebrate, especially to me in 2011. My country had recently invaded Iraq. Beforehand, the idea of invasion was talked about extensively, and I had thought it was crazy, so much so that I believed our president had to be bluffing when he talked about it. In the run-up talk and afterwards, that word "empire" was resurrected from history, though not by the president of course. Did England set out to create an empire "in a fit of absence of mind," as I read somewhere at that time, with horror? British historian J. R. Seeley wrote that in 1883.

I didn't find out until the trip itself that "Empire Builder" was the nickname of James J. Hill, the railroad magnate who made that line happen. He probably loved his nickname. I'm all right about it now, the name. I like it even. The nickname origin helped make it better.

I don't know about our venture into Iraq. Bless all our soldiers, all who served, all who were killed or wounded, all their families and friends. I have never believed, and will never, never believe, that anyone can die "in vain." There is so much we don't understand. There are always things to be learned from anything and everything that happens in this world. I may be wrong, may have been wrong about Iraq. At the least, I believe our president made a principled decision, doing what he thought was right. I fully believe he is and was that kind of man.

I'm grateful to our soldiers. I'd be a pathetic soldier. I'd faint in the heat, cry in the cold, be afraid. Of course I'd be afraid. Bless all the people in Iraq, even the "bad" ones, the ones I would call misguided. Bless our politicians, too. I would never want to be in politics, so I'm glad somebody wants to. Being a leader is not always so easy. I forget this sometimes or most of the time, I forget I even believe it, but I believe we all do our best.

In the weeks before my trip, it was the name of the train from Washington, DC to Chicago, the middle train I was taking on the westward trip out, and ended up taking again coming home, that caused me to make the one exception to letting the itinerary stay folded and untouched. I kept forgetting the name of that train. When I had a free evening, and had chosen to lounge, and was lying stretched out across the bed, I might daydream about the pre-departure meal or the names of the trains, but would never be able to remember that one name. I'd get up and bring the tri-fold over to the bed and lie down again and open it and, carefully, superstitiously, avoiding the dates and times of the trains, would read the names in the headings of the out-going trip. *Crescent*, first, then the *Capitol Limited*. That's the one I couldn't keep in mind. The *Capitol Limited*. Then I'd fold the itinerary again, put it back in its carefully created space, go back to the bed and lie down again and remember. The *Capitol Limited*. The *Capitol Limited*.

CHAPTER 6

Hot Summer Day

The Sunday ride through Virginia countryside continued in its perfect way. We pulled into DC around noon. I followed those who got off, and we walked together into the station. This was going to be good. I was a pro.

Union Station's Central Hall was as I remembered from eighth grade, a cathedral of white, a vast cavern of marble and quiet echoes. I walked through slowly, pausing sometimes to see up high, making the effort to take it all in. I'm a country girl now, and think there's nothing more beautiful than the countryside, but this was wonderful, and it was nice to see it again.

Funny, I said to myself, looking around at all the loveliness. Why are you starting to feel nervous? My answer was immediate. Who knows! But, the answer continued, I know one thing. Your nervousness is worsening because you are thinking that this is a test. You are supposed to find this place both perfectly beautiful and as familiar as home. You are failing the test. You are not losing yourself in the beauty. You are not comfortable.

Don't worry, I said to myself. You'll be alright.

I had already made a simple plan for this station. Good. I had promised myself a treat after the first train. I would check my bags, having assumed there was a check place, and free myself for the layover. I asked around and found it, a tucked-away counter in an alcove down a short hallway. Checking the bags cost twice what I expected, of course, but I didn't hesitate. I was going to take my reward.

The attendant was the nicest young man, Latino. This could have been his first summer job, he was that young. I didn't want to make the calculations and decisions on how long to leave everything, and he said he'd be happy to do that. He looked at my ticket and figured, and told me when to come back. We were both pleased, and I strode away, free.

Not exactly. The nervousness wasn't going away. DC was supposed to be the easiest part of the whole trip. The station was a place I remembered, and I was going to feel at home. That very plan made all this nervousness worse, as I said. If this is so bad, I barely let myself think, what about the rest of the trip? I walked around, compulsively exploring, in a stressed and robotic way, hoping to distract myself. I thought about getting something to eat. There was a fancy restaurant in the main hall and a food court on the floor below. Both looked good, but I was too restless to sit and not hungry anyway. I decided that I needed to get outside and go for a walk. Walk where?

I went back to the main hall and looked for a guard. There were lots of people in uniform, but all of them appeared to be working for the tour bus companies. I didn't want to bother them in their income-making endeavors, and they might not know much about walking anyway. They were in flocks, dressed in their companies' attention-seeking colors, and when I finally spotted a real guard he was standing by himself, in his earth-toned uniform. I quickly walked his way.

"Do you know someplace I can walk to?"

Perhaps I asked too assertively. I believe I did. My anxiety was high and getting higher. I wanted to get out. And surely my question didn't make a lot of sense. He looked "on guard," as if I might be dangerous.

"What do you mean?" he said, frowning, focusing, leaning away from me.

I explained, in as calm and polite and rational a manner as I could muster, that I had a layover and wanted to walk someplace, maybe a half-mile away or so.

"You could walk to the Capitol," he said. He turned and pointed and named the number of blocks. He couldn't entirely conceal a look of annoyance.

The Capitol! What a perfect thing! I thanked him effusively, probably too effusively, and walked in the direction he'd pointed, towards the row of doors that marked the obvious exit to the outside.

Before the beautiful, big, heavy, glass and brass door closed behind me in its slow and stately way, I knew that it was a killer heat day in DC.

Ahead of me was no shade, not one bit of shade, just a large traffic circle around a large island with a mountainous statue in its center. Lots of open space to cross, lots of baking concrete, some cars and busses and exhaust. Not the release I had anticipated. I worked to cheer myself on, like the birds who cheered Peter Rabbit, caught by the buttons of his coat in the gooseberry net of mean Mr. McGregor's garden. You can do this, I said. My heart was beating fast. Deny the power of fear. That is my fear mantra. I kept it on repeat, to ward off fear thoughts. Deny the power of fear. Deny the power of fear. It didn't seem to be working. I was still anxious. Maybe it was keeping things from getting worse. I had another mantra that I had decided beforehand to bring along specifically for the trip, but couldn't remember what it was. I tried to think of it as I crossed the baking hot desert of the traffic circle. One of the words started with "h." I could remember that much. Hope? Heart? Happiness? I couldn't remember. That struck me as funny. The laughing was good. Hah-hah. A person could die in this heat.

I walked at a steady, rapid, purposeful pace. The purpose was twofold: to get out of the sun quickly without running and to give my beating heart something to do. I made it across the circle. A quiet street led in the direction the guard had pointed. There were sidewalks with trees. This was a park area, with grass and plantings and more trees within the parks on both sides of the street. Mercy!

Avoiding the sun completely was impossible, so I made my way with a game of maximizing shade, crossing from side to side. Not that the shade was cool. It wasn't. It was just less hot.

There were no cars. Good. There weren't many people around either. It was almost deserted. Was it because this was Sunday? Washington is a prime tourist place. I would have thought there'd be tourists out. Was it because I was going to the Capitol? Congress probably didn't meet on Sundays. Maybe the Capitol was closed on Sundays. Was it because of the budget disagreement? Was that a factor? Was Congress on vacation? Or was it just too hot for any normal person to be out?

Sometimes I detoured onto one of the gravel paths which meandered through the parks. The paths were shadier than the sidewalks, and walking there was a distracting variation, but I stayed close to the sidewalks and the road. In addition to everything else, I was afraid of getting lost and not getting back to the station on time. A sprinkler was working on one of the paths. I crossed under the rain, doubled back, and went back and forth a few more times. A touch of relief, a touch of the familiar. I never altered my walking speed, keeping the rhythm up without thinking, leaning on the rhythm to keep me going. I played with thoughts of evaporation. Water molecules on my skin and clothes, influenced by both my movement through the air and the heat of me, would be taking off into the air as vapor. They would take some of my heat with them.

After the sprinkler, I returned to the sidewalk and came up behind a little family walking the same direction. I slowed. They were two parents and a boy, and they were discussing the sprinkler. The boy, about six, was saying that he wanted to turn around and go through it. The parents hesitated, the hesitation of stressed hot tourist parents, and said no. He whined a bit and they said no again, more confidently this time, but not meanly. I felt for all three of them. I hoped he hadn't seen me going through the sprinkler. I didn't want to be the cause of this. I also didn't like the slow walking they were doing, so I stepped off into the street and crossed to the other side, resuming my former pace.

I was still anxious. Horribly so. It was so hot. My heart and mind were racing. Why was I so anxious? I got no answer. If I suddenly fell to the sidewalk, I thought, collapsing with heat stroke or a seizure of anxiety, would there be anyone to help me? Do people stop and help anymore? It seemed absurdly funny to think of myself dying in that way. What a way to go. Hah-hah.

I started thinking obsessively about my heart. It seemed, I said to myself as I walked and walked, almost unbelievable that a heart would continue to beat, time after time, in good healthy rhythm, day and night, year after year after year. Would obsessive thinking about a heartbeat interfere with its constancy, its loyalty? I couldn't help wondering. I tried not to think about it, but that made me more conscious of it. This is really nuts, I thought, and I had to laugh, out loud.

"A deranged person, last seen laughing to herself while pacing the concrete sidewalks in the hottest part of the day during our current heat wave, was found collapsed…"

I walked on.

And then, the Capitol. It appeared in the distance. Maybe it saved me. Have you ever seen the Capitol? It is so big and beautiful. I got closer, and without the slightest pause in my walking, I spotted and veered left towards the perfect place, a low wall shaded by one of the few trees in this new territory. I made it to the wall and sat down, facing an enormous parking lot that was practically empty. Far away, across the large lot, rose the Capitol, high up into the sky, and I, released at last, somewhat, sat and took in the scene, and did my best not to think too much.

Anna Raglan

CHAPTER 7

Recovery

M e on the low wall, and in front of me a great stage, the parking lot, with the enormous Capitol at a distance as the backdrop. The spectacular marble Capitol looked translucent in the hazy, shimmery light of the hot humid summer day. Not very solid, but comfortable. An idea. A castle. Comforting. Storybook.

I had my phone and so knew the time, and I had forty-five minutes before I needed to start back. It took a while for my mind to settle. It didn't settle completely, but enough. A group of four mixed-aged adults wandered up and shared the wall space briefly. They conversed among themselves. Where are we going? What should we do? Other than smiles, we made no contact. For me, self-preservation was everything and that meant conservation of energy. No conversations.

There was a guard station on the far right side of the parking lot at its entrance. About every ten minutes a car would pull up to the station, pause, then continue on into the lot and take one of the marked parking spots. Each car had one person, the driver, who got out of the parked car and headed towards the Capitol. Then a guard with a smallish, black, Lab-type dog on a leash came out of the guard house and walked towards the empty car. The Lab was as happy a dog as I've ever seen. Her tail wagged constantly. The guard walked her around the car in a wide circle and her job, I think, was to approach and sniff each door. Sometimes she'd skip a door and her handler would correct her by shooting out his arm and leaning towards the missed one, and she'd go back. Her happy tail never missed a wag. She wasn't the least bit bothered by her mistake or the correction, and she wagged all the way around the car and then back to the guard station.

Meanwhile, the person from the car walked toward the Capitol, and toward a group of five or six people assembled in front of it. I had seen them from the first, and wondered what they were doing. When the car person approached, each lifted what I guessed was a video camera to their shoulder. The car person stopped for a minute, then went into some inconspicuous entrance. I must have been facing a side of the Capitol. I didn't see any grand steps.

Everything was far away. I imagined the conversation between the car person and the video people:

"Any progress on the budget talks?"

"Well, yes..." or "Well, no..." and talk, talk, talk.

I watched the car, guard and dog, and videographer scene repeated a few times, and then my forty-five minutes was over. I got up and started the walk back.

This time I noticed that in the street leading up to the guard house, not the street I was walking on, there were metal barriers that were lowered flush with the street to be driven over, and could presumably be raised to stop something big.

I was wearing black pants. Black is the worst possible color for being outside in the sun on a hot summer day in the South. White is the best color for hotness, but the worst, of course, to show spills and dirt. There were many clothing constraints that I'd come up with pre-trip, and I'd spent a lot of time thinking about clothes, especially the pants.

What would I wear and how much in the way of changes would I carry with me? I decided that I wouldn't count on using anything from my suitcase. Even thinking of getting it down and opening it, much less looking for things, felt crazy. Second, I decided that I could do the whole four days in one pair of pants. I didn't want to carry a lot of extra clothes. So black won because of the spills issue. Also, as the fashion-savvy tell us, black is slimming.

I wanted cotton pants, one hundred percent cotton, because of what I think might be called "breathability," i.e. coolness, and because of feel. I think cotton feels best. But what kind of cotton? I have pants that claim to be one hundred percent, and they are comfortable, but they are knit. Something about them feels sleazy after a while, and I call four days a while. I doubted I would find the right cotton, to say nothing of style and fit. I wanted comfort, but not too much comfort. Too baggy and too stretchy gives way over time to sloppy, which jumps over time to depression, and I didn't want any depression. There was another problem. I don't like to shop. I used to like to shop, but that was long ago.

Avoidance of shopping, in 2011, for the computer-less, meant catalogues. I had a few around. *Deva* was one. It was a hippie kind of a deal, with lots of cotton things, mostly peasant styles, but a lot of straightforward looks, too. *Deva*'s clothes were made by women (I doubt any men) at their own sewing machines in their own homes in Midwest America. I think that's what a cottage industry is. They had some pants called "Tapers," and you could get these in black and in a choice of woven cotton weights. I chose the lightest, "Breezecloth."

They were perfect. I am still surprised. I rarely score with clothes. The pants fit my most succinctly worded travel criteria: like pajamas, but not too much like pajamas. I love them still. I save them for special occasions.

The rest of the clothing decisions were easy. Two patterned shirts, patterned to hide stains. One to wear, one to carry in the pack for a mid-trip change. I had a few of these already to choose from. And a cotton cardigan, aqua, to put on or take off as needed. Comfort, choice.

On my walk back to the station, I paused to check out the subject of the statue in the middle of the traffic circle. It was Columbus and a big round Earth. Columbus

Circle, I supposed. I'd heard of Columbus Circle. I went back into the hall, then downstairs to the food court, foods from around the big round Earth, and bought an Asian wrap and sat and ate half and repackaged the other. Then I went back upstairs to collect my bags. My friend at the counter gave me a gift I will never forget. He had looped the two shoulder straps of my daypack over the extended handle of my roller suitcase, so that my pack sat securely on top of the suitcase and the whole assembly moved as one. It was a gift of freedom, transcendence above chaos, like an authentic spiritual teaching. "Thank you!" I said, so pleased, so grateful, liking him so much, and I gave him a good tip and a hearty farewell.

I rolled my way to the departure area for my next train, the *Capitol Limited*. The heat and the anxiety had left me dazed. Maybe even stunned. But I was OK. I was where I wanted to be and in a protected place, wondering why I hadn't considered that trying to manage a roller suitcase plus two carry-ons in train stations and onto trains might have made me cry.

There were plenty of seats available in the waiting section. I was early, and that was fine. Waiting sounded just right. Waiting can be hard when you are waiting for something you expect to be good, or bad. I wasn't looking ahead.

As I recall, the seats were wooden. If I know people, then someone at some time has looked at those seats and wanted to change them, wanted to make them more comfortable. Some people would want to make the whole area brighter. Not me. I remember half-wall partitions made of a deep-toned brown wood. I like thinking back on the wood. Did the original designers thrill at the combination of white marble and darkish wood? Not only the difference in colors, but also the different sounds and feels, and also the fact that wood was once a tree, and marble was and is a rock? I wasn't thinking of that then. I was getting a pleasant break— a nice seat, restful lighting, and the somewhat distant soothing sounds of shoes and voices on marble.

The next stop for me was to be Chicago. Before the trip, Chicago had been one of my biggest worries. I'd never been there.

CHAPTER 8

Kind People

I'd made a list of worries before the trip because I figured they'd be gone from my mind afterwards. "Stations will be dangerous" was second on the list.

When I thought pre-trip about Chicago, I knew everything would probably be fine, but just in case, my imagination prepared me for the worst. The Chicago train station could be in a bad part of town, the worst part of town, and might look as bad as an old seedy bus terminal, with old yellowish-tan tiles on the walls, and dirty floors. It would be understaffed, with the too-few workers behind glass partitions, pretending not to hear you, so hardened with burn-out and cynicism they would barely help you with basic train questions, and would not help without long contemptuous looks, and would certainly never assist if you got your purse snatched. "What do you want me to do about it, lady?" There probably would be purse snatchers among the lost people who hung about the station, if it were in the worst part of town.

On the sunny summer day of departure, back home in the country, when I had plenty of time to do my packing, I came up with a survival idea. I took a one-hundred dollar bill out of the cash I was going to bring, rolled it up, and sewed it into the bottom of the pocket of my black pants. Just in case. The lightweight cotton of the pants made for easy sewing.

No challenges presented themselves in the quiet Washington Union Station waiting area. I wasn't thinking about Chicago, or anything. I was resting.

The announcement was made for boarding, and we travelers gathered and went through a door into the underground space where our train waited. I got in line and at the door the attendant handed me my seat number. She said I was on the upper level. So this was to be a double-decker train. I hadn't noticed.

There was no stepstool here. The floor inside the train was level with the platform. I walked in, pulling my bags, and saw the steep narrow steps going to the top. I was wondering how to get everything up those steps when I heard a voice from behind me. "Excuse me." I turned to see a woman my age. "Could you help me put my suitcase up on the shelf?" She had a suitcase like mine. "I have a bad back and I can't lift it." I then saw the low shelves. Nobody had to pull anything up the stairs.

"Of course," I said, and I lifted hers up onto the shelf and put mine up too, and we thanked each other. I glanced through the doorway that led straight into the lower level passenger section, felt pity for the people who were so unlucky to be assigned there, and started up the steps. I was going to the top! And there I had a window seat again and the woman behind me was my seatmate. Her name was Allison.

Allison told me that she always asks the seat assignment person to put her with another woman. She had done that ever since the time she sat next to a man who kept putting his hand on her hand or on her knee, even when Allison asked him to stop. "I found the car attendant and asked to be moved," she said.

I was instantly proud to know her. Imagine, I thought. Such mastery of the system! Allison was also going to Chicago.

Passengers were filing in. There was a group of African American men traveling together, wearing identical jackets, athletic type jackets, mostly purple, with some emblems sewn on. Two of the men sat in the seats ahead of us across the aisle. From their talk, I gathered that they'd been to a convention in Washington connected with the anniversary of the founding of a fraternity at Howard University. They'd had a good time, it seemed. Their talk was jovial.

Things were great once more for me as well. I had the unexpected surprise of a double decker train, a window seat on top, a nice seatmate, and the radiating cheer of the good talk in the car from the convention men. The men joked with each other in a natural brotherly way, not in an attention-getting way. I gathered that the fraternity was celebrating one hundred years.

So that would be 1911. That was only forty-seven years after the end of, God help us, slavery.

Pretty soon an Amtrak employee came and stood in the aisle and gave us a welcome and information speech. He also gave us a kind of general apology. It was as much defense as apology. "If you knew me you'd know I'm the nicest kind of guy you'd ever meet!" I believed him. I believed I'd be happy to know him. Apparently there had been a confrontation and, though he gave no details, whatever happened must have been public, prompting a public response. He was a little wired. I felt for him. I get wired, too. And if you're in a business that deals with deadlines and the public, and you want to do a good job, then you're probably going to get wired and you're certainly going to make mistakes, being human, and sometimes people are going to think you've made mistakes when you haven't really.

He finished his defense and apology, then started talking about direction on a moving train, about how not to get confused when you've gotten up and gone somewhere and want to get back to your seat. He illustrated his talk with some directional hand motions. "It's really very simple," he said, and then said some things about if the train is going THIS way and you want to go THIS way back … I had quit paying attention to the words by then because it sounded too confusing for a vacation, direction not being an area where I shine. I got his number on one thing, though: People getting lost on a train pushed his button. Slow breath, buddy. It'll be alright. I liked him. He was trying to help. He had that friendly boyish quality I fall for, but with a stressed edge. He was cute, too. Maybe it was Thomas, doing double duty, having a change from the phones, and having a bad day.

Another man, young, came by to check tickets. He took mine, read it, and looked over at me with a quick happy recognition. "You're from Greenville?" he asked. Yes, I said, then explained that I actually lived two hours away. That was close enough. "I'm from there," he said. "I started out on the *Crescent* and then they transferred me here." He missed home. You could tell. It was a good interchange for both of us.

The train had started. Allison and I, two women of the same age, traveling alone, became friends easily. She lived outside Baltimore and taught religion in a Catholic school. She was knowledgeable and she was calm.

I know a few Catholics. They range from lapsed to devout. Some of the lapsed might not call themselves Catholic, they might call themselves ex-Catholics, and might take offense at my calling them Catholic. I think of them as Catholic because they had in common the religious schools and Communion and Confession and saints and Mass and the big families. Who could say that those experiences were all great or all bad? I call them Catholic because my mental picture of that upbringing makes them so. The picture I have happens to be benign.

None of my devout Catholic friends, and there are three of those, are showy in their devotion, or pushy, and none take the whole story. The most enthusiastic of the devout three, the only convert, doesn't take the part that if you commit suicide you go to hell. I found that out when I was telling him about a friend who killed himself, and how surprised and sad I was. I was adrift in the delicate telling, and I just tossed out, respectfully, "I know you believe he's in hell but I don't," and my devout friend surprised me by saying that he didn't really believe that either. I had assumed he believed it all.

I don't tend to discuss religion with my friends. It can be tricky. One time I happened to be talking about Catholicism with my second devout friend, and I mentioned, respectfully, because she was a friend and I did respect her and I also didn't want to make her mad, that Catholicism was OK with me, but I had trouble with the part about the pope being infallible. It didn't make sense that any person was infallible. She waved her hand. "Oh, the pope," she said.

I love my Catholic friends. They get as discouraged as anyone, but seem to know a way out from discouragement. As a group they are a lively bunch. They laugh easily. Some make jokes, and they all do helpful things, and they think about things. One of my lapsed friends takes "The Catholic Worker" and does as much to help people as anybody I know. She's a natural helper. She told me recently, with great excitement, that her gay sister's marriage had been blessed by a priest. I don't know any practicing gay Catholics, but I've heard of a group of very devout ones. You take what you need and leave the rest. That's what I think. You do your best.

One of Dee's friends, raised Catholic, calls himself a recovering Catholic and recently began attending Mass again. He sits down and checks out the other people, then thinks about our common humanity. When the Mass starts, he lets the rhythm and feel of the sights and sounds carry him for the hour. The words, other than his own initial and sometimes repeated contemplation of humanity, mean little or nothing to him. This thing that I do, he says, may seem insignificant, but nowhere else in my week do I step outside of my world to do that kind of contemplation.

My seatmate Allison reminded me of my third devout Catholic friend. They both seemed to have it together. They had a quiet inner strength. My devout friend was so kind, and had an easy-going wisdom. She worked with children, like Allison, and, like Allison, felt good about her work. One time my devout friend started to grouse about a priest she considered arrogant, but she passed over that quickly with her effortless laugh. She had learned to keep her mind headed in a positive direction. She died before the predator priest scandal became widely known. She died of cancer twenty-five years ago, and died bravely, keeping her kindness and humor as much as anyone could. She still lives in my heart, in my thoughts. I picture her and smile, and am encouraged.

CHAPTER 9

What A Poet And
The Scientists Say

"North Carolina?"

Allison was more interested than one might expect when I answered her question of where I lived.

"Yes," I said.

Allison was one of those Catholics who cares deeply about the poor. There was a well-known North Carolina politician who cared as well, or said he did. I believed him. Then he got seduced by wealth and whatever else, and lost his bearing. It happens a lot. It could happen to anyone.

"I arrive every second," says poet Thich Nhat Hanh. "I am the frog," "a tiny bird," "a caterpillar," "a jewel hiding itself in a stone." "I am the pirate, my heart not yet capable of seeing and loving."

Allison had her hopes up for this politician who could speak about the institutional barriers to the escape from poverty, and her hopes had been dashed. We sighed about the disappointments of politics, a sigh anyone could make, and we went from there to our fathers. We both had kind fathers. Mine had died many years previously, of an aortic aneurism, right at the time my devout Catholic friend, the one I told you about who died, found out she had cancer. When my dad died, he and I were living eight hours apart. Both of us had full lives. He'd been relatively healthy up to his death and had been living in a good situation for an old man, with someone, my mother, who took good care of him. In the last years of their life together, he'd get up early, and my mother would sleep in, and they'd reverse that at night. That's one way to do it. My father had friends he loved and got together with them often, usually with cocktails. The aneurism happened, and that was it. His wasn't a difficult death for me. He was not in my daily life. Our time together had been when I was young and he'd been a terrific dad for me then. There was little fanfare to our relationship. I just trusted him. He had a genuine smile and a genuine laugh, and I knew he enjoyed my company, for the most part. I can look back and see the difficulties he had, but he did not display his worry. I am so thankful for all of it.

Allison's father had been a great dad, too, but had died only recently, and she had been one of his caretakers. We had lots to talk about there. I'm not saying her grief was terrible. Maybe it was or maybe it wasn't. She didn't say. But her dad was on her mind during the time of our ride together. She told me stories about him. He was her rock during a difficult time she'd had as an adult, and she had cared for him tenderly at the end. She was missing him. It goes without saying that we each had other more challenging relationships in our lives. We breezed over one or two of those, smiled about them, and left them behind. Works in progress. I think we would have agreed on that.

Then it was dinnertime. Allison asked what I was going to do, and I told her I had a half wrap left over from lunch. She said she wasn't very hungry and was not going to go to the Dining Car but just to the Snack Bar. Allison was a train pro.

She left, and I ate the rest of my Asian wrap, looking out the window and feeling good. When she came back, she said there was less choice than there used to be. She had been thinking of one thing, maybe a salad, and had to settle for something else.

Allison made this trip once or twice a year. She had family in the Midwest. "Why do you take the train?" I asked. She took the train because she was afraid of flying. She wasn't impossibly afraid. She'd taken her mother once to France and they'd flown. But the train was much easier for her.

"Are you afraid of flying?" she asked me.

"No," I said. Then there was a pause, and then I said, "I'm going to tell you why I'm taking the train, and you're the first person I'm telling." She looked at me expectantly.

"I'm a scientist," I said.

Dear Allison. She was so kind. She just kept her expectant look and waited. I could see that more was needed. "An environmentalist," I added. And still she was kind.

"I used to give to Greenpeace," she said, enthusiastically, supportively.

So I kept going. I said that because I was a scientist, meaning not that I worked in a laboratory wearing a long white coat, like the mental picture you have when someone says scientist, or even that I was employed as a scientist, which I wasn't, but meaning that I was interested in science, to a degree, and that I *believed*, mostly, what scientists said, if there was some consensus, and, well, then, *because* I called myself a scientist and *because* I believed there was remarkable consensus among scientists about global warming, then I had to believe in it. Allison nodded.

I then went on to what I was sure she knew, but maybe didn't have at the forefront of her mind, that train travel is less energy consumptive than air travel. Since I knew this fact, and could also get three weeks off, then it was important to me that I travel to Seattle by train.

Allison didn't comment on the "I'm a scientist" line, it probably wasn't at all clear what I meant, but she did speak about the energy efficiency part. She didn't know about trains being more efficient than planes. She had never needed to think about it. "I'm going to tell my kids," she said, with feeling.

"Yes," I said, whipped up. "It's kind of obvious if you ever stop to think about it. It takes more energy to get off the ground than it does to roll along."

As a way to explain my choice of traveling by train, "I'm a scientist" fell flat, and I haven't used it since. Honestly, I thought the response would be obvious. "I'm a scientist" would be the same thing as "I believe in science." It would be heard as a statement of belief instead of occupation, and the connection to global warming would quickly follow. I don't know why I assumed those things. I'm grateful that I had such a generous audience in Allison.

Almost everyone who considers science a belief, believes that the earth is warming, and that changes will continue to accumulate and disrupt. I love what the unwieldy word "environmentalist" means. I love nature and want to live in a healthy nature. I love what "ecology" means, the idea of all life as a web, with all its interworkings, known and unknown, essential and crucial. "Earth systems science" is a new phrase for me, introduced to me by scientist and conservationist Tim Flannery. It is "the holistic study of how our planet works," as he says in his book *Here on Earth,* and this new way of study sounds adventuresome. Whatever the words, the truth is that we are part of the whole.

That was it for science. Allison and I talked about some other things, and then it was time for sleep. She told me that the bathrooms were on the first level, and we took turns so that we could watch each other's things. When we were both back at our seats, she showed me how to work my footrest. We unfolded our blankets and leaned our seats back. We'd already gotten our pillows when they had been handed out earlier. I didn't get out my own pillow. Then Allison closed her eyes. I marveled at her ability to be so still. I think she went right to sleep. Maybe she had trained herself. It took a while for me. I felt restless.

CHAPTER 10

Allison And Me

In the morning after we'd been awake a bit, Allison said she was going to the Dining Car for breakfast. I asked if it was all right if I went along, and she said, "Of course."

We got out of our seats, and I followed her through the aisle to the door of the car. Did we walk forward or back? I don't remember. Did I pay attention, as our car attendant had recommended? No, I did not. "Thank you for thinking for me," I could have said to Allison.

At the door she demonstrated her preferred method of opening doors between trains. There was a slim metal vertical rod attached to the left frame and she grabbed that with her left hand and kicked with her right foot a plate on the door marked "Open," and the metal door slid rapidly aside for us.

"I don't have to touch the hand plate that way," she said. I had opened the door for the smoke stop in Virginia, but I had used the higher hand plate. Never again! I wasn't bothered by the thought of germs. I wanted the look. I wanted the footwork of her technique, her graceful moves, the confident way she managed the metal door.

We walked through two or three cars to get to the Dining Car, then stood in the doorway until someone came to seat us. There were booths on either side. It was perfect. There were table cloths, real plates, real forks, spoons and knives. We were seated across from a man and his seven-year-old grandson, and we started a friendly conversation right off. There was another grandson back in their sleeper car, a fourteen-year-old, too sleepy, or maybe playing too cool, to want to get up and eat breakfast. This was a vacation trip. The grandfather had taken the boys to Washington, and the train travel was part of the fun. With a sleeper, I learned, your Dining Car meals are free. I was so excited to be in the passenger train Dining Car, to have it be perfect, to have great breakfast companions, and I had to restrain myself from being wildly talkative.

We talked about sightseeing in Washington. The boy's favorite thing had been the Washington Monument, climbing the stairs to the top.

I almost ordered French toast. It's the famous train breakfast, apparently. The boy ordered it, and it did look good. I had an omelet, which was very good, but skipped the coffee. I had decided to avoid caffeine for the three or four days, hoping I'd sleep better. I was tempted, especially because the cups were china, not paper. A cup of coffee, hard to resist. A real cup, brought to me by a friendly person, here on the train, with good company and all the time in the world. But it was not too hard to resist. Everything else was so good.

Back at our seats, Allison and I were quiet for a while. The fraternity gentlemen sitting on the other side of the aisle were talking about their neighborhoods, how much they enjoyed them, the different things they did in their neighborhood groups. One of them wondered aloud why some young people wanted to be destructive rather than constructive. "It doesn't make any sense to me," he said. One of their friends sitting somewhere ahead came back to visit them, standing in the aisle to talk. More neighborliness. I loved it, and wondered about their fraternity, celebrating one hundred years. Imagine the power, the love, the heartache, the goodness, the sense of family in a Black fraternity at a Black college in the United States in 1911. And, oh sure, an argument or two. They were family after all. But any conflict would have been nothing compared to the goodness.

I watched out the window. "How do you get to be on the top?" I asked Allison. She said that people usually want to be on the bottom. They don't want to climb the stairs. She, like me, loved the top. She said that the train from New York to Chicago was only a single level because the tunnels it had to go through weren't high enough for the double-decker. So we were grateful.

She started telling me all the train things she could think of. She asked if I was ever going to eat dinner. Oh, yes, I said. "Get the chicken," she said. "It's good."

"How many times have you taken this trip?"

She paused and looked into the middle distance, the way relaxed and truthful people do, to tally an accurate number. "About thirty," she said.

She told me that if I ever got a seatmate who smelled bad, I could find the attendant and ask to be moved. That was reassuring. I'd been a little concerned about smells.

She said you have to be easy-going to ride the train, because of the delays.

As we got close to Chicago, she described the station for me. "It's different from the Washington station," she said, "and it can be confusing at first."

We talked about Chicago food. It was now near lunchtime. She loved "Chicago dogs," the famous hot-dogs. She was going to get one for lunch, and I said that sounded good to me, too. "Pizza is also good," she said. The deep-dish Chicago pizza.

Just like in DC, the train in Chicago stops underground. Allison and I left our seats and walked down the steep stairs to the first level and picked up our suitcases. Once we stepped outside the comfortable train, we entered what someone might have constructed as their vision of a walk through hell. The platform walkway was, of course, well-lit, but surrounding us was dark tunnel, big and deep, with big trains and lots of loud train noises—brakes screeching and I don't know what else. It was hot and humid, with a touch of grime in the air. It was very exciting. There was so much other-worldliness. Again, I had Allison to thank for liking this so much. I was just following her. I had no anxieties about where to go. I followed her along the platform and we made our way in a crowd of fellow passengers to the station.

Inside, she turned to me. "Do you want a tour?" What a gift! Of course I did! We went first to the food area for lunch, and Allison found an empty table, which wasn't simple because there were so many people eating and milling around. She watched my bags while I went to Gold Coast Dogs and ordered a hotdog with all the things on it that made it a Chicago Dog, and then I watched her bags while she did the same. I waited until she came back before I started to eat. If you like a hotdog with lots on it, and I do, then you would like the Chicago one.

Then came the tour. She showed me the Amtrak waiting rooms, there were two, and other things, all a blur to me now, and then up or down some stairs and to the Great Hall. She was excited about that and had saved it for last. She seemed proud of it, as if the Chicago station were partly hers. I had not told her how afraid I had been of my layover there.

To her pronounced disappointment, the lovely, high-ceilinged hall was in use. "What? Where are the benches?" We stood at the entrance. You could pass around the outer edge, and a few people were doing that, but the central area where you would usually sit was roped off. There had been an event sponsored by something called Skinny Cow, which I had never heard of, and now the hall was empty, except for those walking around the sides and one young man who was tending to the breakdown. "It's such a nice place to sit," Allison said, looking around in disbelief.

I, on the other hand, was staring at two modern, inviting, arm-less sofas in the far right corner of the roped-off area. They looked as if they had been brought in as part of the event décor and, if so, it is no surprise that they looked inviting. The promoters of Skinny Cow—a company confident enough to engage the central hall of the Chicago train station and therefore certainly confident enough to hire people who are very effective at persuasion—had chosen those sofas to be inviting. How roped off were they? Not completely.

In place were those velvet rope systems with sturdy, heavy, moveable stands that are used to control polite crowds, and the stands and ropes were now placed to give the clear impression that the party was over. There were, however, adequate gaps between the sets. A person could easily walk into the roped-off area without moving any stand or stepping over any rope. My rebellious side, dormant for so long, was alert and rubbing her hands.

"Let's just go sit over there," I suggested. Allison looked at the sofas. The busy young man, folding chairs or something, was way over in the opposite corner of the roped-off area, and this was a big place. She hesitated.

"OK," she said. We walked through an opening and over to the sofas, and sat down. I acted nonchalant. We enjoyed the comfort of the sofas and the beauty of the impressive hall for about fifteen seconds before the young man, whom we weren't watching, apparently spotted us. We saw him as he came hurrying our way, with a clear look of irritation on his face.

"You can't sit there!" he said. "You can't be in here!" He waved his hands rapidly to indicate the forbidden area.

"Oh," I said. "Sorry!" My "oh" was an ambiguous one, partly a neutral and truthful acknowledgement, partly a feigning of innocence. Somewhat of a question, to emphasize the innocent part. "Oh?"

My "sorry" was half sincere, but delivered as completely sincere. I really was sorry we had inconvenienced him. He was, after all, doing a job that was probably not completely fun and we were obviously making it less so. But I wasn't sorry we'd sat on the sofas. It was fun being the leader, being rebellious, having a compadre. And it was fun being the only ones sitting, luxuriously at that, in the Grand Hall of Chicago's Union Station. I apologized again, and we got up and left.

Thinking about this three years later, as I write, I'm not so comfortable about what I did. I hate to say this about myself, but I do understand why some people get a kick out of being destructive. I send the young man thoughts of apology, and, just in case he needs it, of strength. And, OK, a few laughs to share, but only if he wants them. Maybe we could even join forces. He could pick something he was not proud of. He could accept his responsibility if he hadn't already done so, and we could fling our somethings into the air. They would attract each other, like matter and anti-matter, they would collide, and then Poof! Gone. Freedom for him, freedom for me. Ahhh. I think things like that are possible.

CHAPTER 11

Chicago Has A River

Chicago and Washington both have big beautiful train stations named Union. Was "union" a word so powerful in the railroad age that it could proudly be used twice?

The famous big New York City train station is named Penn, as are a number of other stations in the Northeast. My friend David, in my writer's group, laughed when I mentioned this. "Lead us not into Penn Station," he said. That was a joke from his childhood.

Allison and I left the Hall, headed to the Amtrak waiting area, and the busyness of the place became apparent. I think the station was a bus and subway terminal as well as a train station. Most people were walking with intensity, and I was glad to be at ease. Allison was taking another train to somewhere south of Chicago. Our trains were supposed to leave at about the same time, two hours away, but from the different waiting rooms, which were next to each other. We went into mine. "Goodbye," she said. "I'm going on over to the other waiting room. I hope the rest of your trip goes well."

"Thank you," I said, and we hugged each other. "Thank you so much for the tour and for all the train advice. I really appreciate it. I hope your trip goes well, too." And then she left.

I was shocked. Maybe it showed. I hope it didn't. Maybe I even really said, "Our trains don't leave for two hours," meaning, aren't we going to sit together until then? I can't remember, or maybe I don't want to remember. But I remember the shock, the ol' human jolt of feeling rejected.

I was alone, but I was a big girl. I had been to the school of life. I knew that feeling rejected was a ridiculous response and I gave myself a consoling pat on the back. Bless Allison, she'd probably had her fill of being leader. Maybe she just needed some quiet time. Maybe the Great Hall silliness wasn't to her liking or maybe she had burdens, or chores. Bless her. I sat with this a bit, then took in my surroundings.

Amtrak Waiting Room A, or maybe it was B, was a big room, not huge, and it was strictly functional. Nothing ornate. There was a small fixed sign on the wall with slots for departure announcements. There I saw "Empire Builder," printed simply on a removable insert, which was just right, because it was exciting enough seeing those words again, appearing in a more concrete world this time. Maybe this wasn't storybook. Maybe there really was a train called *Empire Builder*, and a city called Seattle.

I listened, and listened again, to the loudspeaker message that repeated every five minutes or so, about reporting suspicious behavior and about the official dog who might be coming around to sniff, and I tried to think of ways to make this announcement repetition amusing, in the way that a good absurdist theatre production can be amusing. Back home, a few years ago, a local director of some renown chose *Old Times* as the final play of his directorial career. It's the only absurdist theatre production I've ever seen, but for me it was enough. I saw it three times, can't imagine there being any better. He probably had his pick of actors, who were excellent.

Beyond the humor to be found in the repeating announcements, I was fully grateful for the people out there working for our safety. I would enjoy getting to know those dog handlers. I like dogs. After sitting a while, I got my phone out of my pocketbook and taught myself how to take pictures.

The few of us in the room were all spread out. The person nearest to me, a woman, got up and came over and asked if I'd watch her luggage while she went to get something to eat. "I'm going to get take-out," she said, letting me know in that way that she wouldn't be gone long.

"Oh, sure," I said.

That must be one of the rules of civility for travel, I thought. A considerate traveler limits her time when she has asked someone to watch her baggage. The modern rule about not watching anyone's luggage did not enter my mind. The woman was gone twenty minutes, and when she came back carrying her paper bag, I asked if she would watch my things. While she had gone to get her take-out, I'd made a plan.

My idea was simple. I would wander around, would try hard to remember how to get back, but I would not worry because I could ask directions to the Amtrak waiting rooms if need be. My mission would be to look for an exit to the outside. I would step into Chicago. It was something to do.

Out of the waiting room, into the open ticket counter area, down a passageway, up or down stairs or escalators, whatever it was, I finally spotted a row of doors to the outside. The doors led to a small piazza, which led to, of all magical things, a pedestrian bridge over a river. Right there.

I walked out onto the bridge, breathed deeply and grinned. I pulled out my cell phone and got ready to take my first ever cell phone picture. "River in Chicago." Then, lo and behold, a nice young man passing by stopped and asked if I wanted to be in the picture and of course I did. "Chicago!"

Back in the waiting room, passengers were gathering for a train, not the *Empire Builder*. Seats were filling. I made friends with an older woman who sat next to me, and who showed me, only after I asked, the pictures of her two grandchildren. One photo was of a smiling young girl posing in a ballerina costume, and the other of a young boy, serious, in a football uniform. I felt happy for the children that they had such a loving grandmother and happy for America and the world. Loving grandmothers make a difference. Her train was called and she left, and now all of us were waiting for the same train.

A woman my age sat beside me and we, too, made friends. She was going home to La Crosse, where the train crosses the Mississippi River. She was proud of that. Watch out for it, she said, meaning the crossing, and I was glad that she did. She said that afterwards I'd be riding alongside the river for a long time, which was a surprise to me. In the South, going cross-country, the Mississippi is a big bridge and a big event. It's anticipated, and then it's done, and the river is over. You have crossed from the East to the West, or vice versa.

My new friend had once crossed paths with the radio host and storyteller Garrison Keillor, whom we both enjoyed. She was shopping in a store in the Mall of America and heard his familiar voice and turned and there he was. I would never have imagined he'd go there. But in one of my favorite stories, he has Pastor Ingqvist leaving the town of Lake Wobegon after so many years and becoming mall chaplain for the very Mall of America. Mall chaplain! It makes me laugh. There should be mall chaplains!

For years I turned on the radio at six o'clock on Saturdays and listened to Garrison's stories of Lake

Wobegon, the Minnesota town found, or not found, in tiny Mist County, which itself is not found on any map because the original surveyors were incompetent and "omitted fifty square miles of central Minnesota." And so it continues to go for Lake Wobegon, whose town motto is "We are what we are."

Garrison saved me from unhappiness on many a Saturday night. Often convinced that I was living the world's dullest life, he shed his light of intelligence and fun on ordinariness, making it anything but ordinary, and helped me see life with new eyes. Who would not be grateful for such a gift?

There was a large Amish group waiting, all ages. Allison had told me that the Amish liked to travel and liked trains. They looked fascinating, especially the children, and I had to tell myself not to stare. No Amish live anywhere near me. I admire them and am glad someone in America knows a simpler way of living than my way, because I hope most of us will want to live more simply someday, and we could learn some things. Two beautiful girls who looked like sisters, dressed exactly alike in pale grey cotton dresses with long sleeves, just like all the other females in the group, sat on the other side of the room in seats that faced mine. They talked together with lots of smiles, and then one put her head in the other's lap and closed her eyes. We were all passing the time in our different waiting ways.

When it was time to board, they called for us in groups and my group, those going to Seattle, the end of the line for the *Empire Builder*, was last. We had our own car. I climbed the narrow stairs to the top again and looked for a seat. There were no assignments because there weren't many of us. My own seat, a thrill and a luxury! I unpacked a few things and spread out.

We got under way, and soon after someone came by taking reservations for dinner. Only the last slot, eight-thirty, was left, but that fit because I like to eat what Americans call "late." And then I got to do what I wanted. I spent a lot of time looking out the window. I remember that, but I don't remember what I saw.

CHAPTER 12

The *Empire Builder*

I relaxed and watched out the window for a long time. Then I got up to explore and found the great Observation Car, the last car on the train, completely windowed on the sides and ceiling, and with two rows of seats facing the outside, one row facing north, the other facing south. I sat looking southward and listened to conversations in the car, then went back to my private seat.

A woman came on the loudspeaker periodically to invite us to the Snack Bar. "Come on down!" she said. She put her all into the invitations, really wanting us to make the trip. "Ladies and Gentlemen!" she called us. She would pour us a Seven and Seven, she said. Maybe Snack Bar wasn't the real name. It was obviously a bar for alcoholic drinks as well. "And for my Heineken lovers, I have a whole case in the refrigerator!" She told us she was on the deck below the Observation Car. "I'm the lady! Come on down." When it was time to get up and move around again I set out to find her. Sure enough, there were narrow stairs in the middle of the Observation Car leading to a small space that had a few booths and a counter. A group of teens, dressed sloppy-hip, played cards at one of the booths and seemed to be having a good time. So that's where the teens go, I thought.

I ordered a cranberry juice. The woman at the bar wasn't as happy as I had pictured. Maybe I was the only one who showed up and maybe she was further disappointed that I didn't order an alcoholic drink. A bartender wouldn't expect much of a tip from a cranberry juice. I understood all that. I worked for many a tip in my younger days, and before I knew what was happening, way back then, my young self started to turn cynical, started to dislike people, to think too much of the troublesome ones, to think too much of what tip I would or wouldn't get. I gave the Snack Bar lady a dollar tip. She deserved every bit of that, for all the effort she was making. The plastic cup she gave me for my canned cranberry juice was an official Amtrak cup. "Rail Consumes Less Energy Than Cars or Air Travel" it said. I still have that cup, somewhere.

From what I've heard, in the old days there was a Smoking Car on the train, and that was where the bar was located. Maybe it was called the Club Car. Stories were both told and born there, no doubt.

I have a good-natured friend who has lived in the same place in rural America all her life. She grew up on a farm, one of eleven children, and married a neighboring young farmer and, with an unfailingly authentic good attitude, did all the farm wife work and church work you could think of. She still does. She is a wonder to behold. Her farmer husband joined the Navy for a brief stint in the sixties, and my friend traveled by train with him once to the West Coast, where he was stationed. She mentioned the Smoking Car in a conversation we had about the train, and just started laughing. I smiled. I didn't feel the need to ask. I think she'd overheard or met some talkers, of the type that a smoking and bar car on a long-distance train would attract, of the type found here and there in every Charles Portis novel, the type who goes on and on about past escapades or schemes for the future.

People boarded the train at the different stops, and at Milwaukee I got a seatmate, the friendliest young man. He told me he was glad to be going home. He was in school in La Crosse and "that's home to me," he said, implying that it was more comfortable there than wherever it was his family lived. I asked him what grade he was in and he said "Senior." Senior in high school, I assumed. He looked so young. But then he said he'd been an accountant. Accounting wasn't right for him—too demanding, he said—and he'd gone back to school in business management

There is a movie I love called *The Lunchbox*. It takes place in India and tells the story of a young woman who cooks in her tiny kitchen, learning about spices from her neighbor Auntie, and who packs lunch for her husband every day. You see bits of her daily life, happy until the difficulties in the marriage begin to surface. Also in the story are two accountants, one a fine accountant nearing retirement and the other young and incompetent, newly hired. The young accountant is big-hearted, and optimistically determined to break away from his bleak past on all fronts. You suspect as you watch that he will end up alright, because his genuine friendliness is the perfect cure for the emotional walls of the older man, who will teach him accounting. The two work in a huge room full of accountants, with wooden desks pushed close, and aisles going this way and that, between and along the islands of desks.

To me it looked like a pleasant office. You could do your accounting work quietly but not feel alone. I like wooden desks. Both men, by the way, had their own love and heartache stories. There's a lot to this movie, including the food aspect. I saw The Lunchbox in a movie theatre and as we viewers got up to leave afterwards, I heard a group of young people decide to go right away to an Indian restaurant.

I liked my new seatmate friend so much that I cast about for a way to demonstrate that and offered to share my cranberry juice. He could have the half that was left in the can. He laughed and said, "No, thank you." We were together for three hours and then he got off at La Crosse. We made each other laugh.

And there was the Mississippi River, at La Crosse, as promised. We rode over, then alongside it for a long time, as promised. What a wonderful thing, to do just that. The river of stories. I watched it for a beautifully long and thought-free time, then got out my phone, took pictures, figured out how to send them, and sent them to Francie and to Nina. Dee's phone couldn't receive pictures. It didn't have a camera. I went back to the Observation Car and took a picture of the car from the entrance and sent that as well. Then I composed a text message about my "train pro friend" Allison, mentioning that she was a schoolteacher, and sent that, including to Dee. "She sounds normal!" one of them responded. "Yes! She was!" I answered back.

A loudspeaker messenger, not the Snack Bar lady, called the eight-thirty reservations to the Dining Car, which was forward on the train. I was shown to a seat in a booth beside a woman from New York City and across from a young couple from Milwaukee. The woman beside me, Asian, was my age and going to Seattle for a family wedding. She was afraid of flying. The young couple was headed to Portland for a bicycle vacation. Their bikes were disassembled, boxed, and with the checked luggage on our train. The couple was going to stay at a bicycle-centered B&B that was also a repair shop, and the mechanic there would put the bikes back together again. The wife had planned the trip and given it as a gift to her husband. He was as happy as could be and talked about how much fun he thought the train was. They had a sleeper. "I brought a book, but so far I just want to look out the window." I was glad he said that. I had wondered, a little, if there was something wrong with me for liking to look out the window so much.

His wife was more reserved. Maybe even unfriendly. That's how I pegged her, I'm afraid. Or, more precisely, "She doesn't like me." I could have been wrong. Regardless, right or wrong, this time I forgot that I was a big girl and broke one of the cardinal rules for happiness: Don't take things personally. I "retaliated" by becoming extravagant friends with the woman beside me, who worked in a city hospital and was in charge of scheduling the Operating Room.

I could imagine right away the pressures of that job. You have the patients and their families who are anxious about the surgery and when it's going to happen, the surgeons and nurses who might have tensions about the same thing, the hospital wanting all to go right and wanting efficient use of their spaces so that profits would be healthy.

"There are a lot of pressures," I said, and she agreed. Maybe she loved her job and was skilled at it and was appreciated, but then our food came and I didn't ask her. I'd ordered the baked chicken and it was indeed good. I also had a glass of wine. It was a perfect dinner and set the pattern for the rest of the train traveling—dinner and a glass of wine at eight-thirty, finishing the day.

I walked back to my seat happy and wined-up, passing through two or three cars and ignoring the bad angel voice in my head singing, "You're never going to find your se-e-eat." In "The Twilight Zone" I wouldn't be able to find it, ever. My neighbor across the aisle was tall and wore a baseball hat with "Air Force" written across the front, and I was grateful he was so recognizable. "Air Force Hat" I called him, to myself. We hadn't spoken. I spotted him easily and smiled, and he smiled back and I slipped into my home. Lights were turned down, pillows handed out, blankets unpacked. All was well.

In the middle of the night I got another seatmate, a solid young man with dreadlocks and a lovely face. He joined me quietly. The car was dark and hushed, and we didn't speak. After a while he got out his cell phone and began a long conversation. He was the quietest cell phone talker I have ever been around. I didn't hear a single word he said, just the soft noise of his low voice. It might even have been another language. I felt reassured about the future of humanity that a person could talk so quietly on a cell phone. He was there for a few hours. I slept some. When he got up quietly at one of our stops, I said a quiet goodbye and he said a quiet one too, laughing a little, and he left. It was still dark.

CHAPTER 13

Good Morning, How Are Ya?

Just before dawn I got my third nighttime seatmate, a girl about twelve. As she and her mother and younger sister made their slow, huddled way down the aisle, the mother murmured for her to take the empty seat beside me, and she did.

She looked worried. Even in the dim light I could tell. Her mother might have judged me benign, but to her I was just a scary stranger. She'd been abandoned, and, to make things worse, Mother and little sister were going to be together. I'd been a shy child. I gave her a smile, not so strong as to alarm her, then chatted a bit, asking simple questions. She was Carrie. We got along fine.

When it began to get light there was something brand new to see—grassland. Rolling hills, and golden, early light of day grassland, with not a building around. Distance, the invitation for gazing. We were in the West.

There was a surprising richness to the grass. It looked deep and thick and tousled, and was fired to a perfect gold by the rising sun. You could see the grass details best on the banks of some little lakes that we passed, which were close to the train. The grasses at lake edge crowded in a wild array, bunches standing straight up beside bunches lying over and others bent over the water.

The grasses and the hills were beautiful, but the lakes were the real surprise. I had never seen anything like them, and I hadn't expected them. Who thinks of lakes on a prairie? Not me. They were small, maybe averaging an acre, and were either single or in small groups. Some had one or two brightly colored ducks floating on the water, breathtakingly beautiful jewels. The grasses, as I said, came right up to the edge. There was no beach or mud. It was wild.

We must still be in Minnesota, I thought. Isn't that the land of ten thousand lakes?

The excitement of the lakes made me restless. Though having a stream of seatmates had been entertaining, I was suddenly tired of my seat and wanted to be alone. I told Carrie I was going to the Observation Car. Did she know about it? No, she didn't. I told her, and then I left.

In the Car were two small groups, already revved up for the day, talking and laughing, and two people lying down. That was the second surprise of the morning. Seats in the Observation Car were in clusters of two or three, so if you wanted to stretch out, apparently you could come in the night, claim an empty group of three seats, and have a bed of sorts.

I sat down by myself, looked out the window, and one of the two conversations grabbed me immediately. Someone who sounded like he used to work for the railroad was talking to a young couple about the very lakes that had surprised me. "I rode this train when I was a boy," he was saying, "and they weren't there." He didn't say anything else about the lakes. They talked about other things, and after a while the young couple got up and left.

I looked over at the man, who was staring out the window. Then I made myself get up and go over to the seat beside him. Not directly beside him. Between some of the seats there was a small built-in table. We had the table between us. "Excuse me," I said. He turned my way. "I just heard you say these lakes didn't used to be here...?"

"No," he said, "they weren't. This land used to be dry. From the fifties to the nineties it was dry."

I didn't know a whole lot about lakes in the Southeast, but I was pretty sure we didn't have anything like that, lakes that came and went. Really? I said. He nodded, then went on. This was flooding from Devil's Lake. There are periods, years, of wet weather and periods of dry. 2011 was a particularly wet year in a wet period. So wet, in fact, that the *Empire Builder* had stopped running for weeks. What? Third surprise. And we were not in Minnesota, we were in North Dakota. Fourth surprise.

The *Empire Builder* had suspended its run, he told me, because of the flooding. It hadn't run for weeks, he repeated. The train we were on was only the second one since the suspension. All this time I had been riding along, innocently unaware how fortunate I was to be riding at all. I remembered that I had heard something in the news about flooding in the West. But why would the train be held up for weeks? Certainly the flood stage levels of water would have receded. Maybe there'd be big puddles, but...

"Why couldn't the train just shoot through the water like you ride a bicycle through a puddle?"

"Because the water makes the ground soft. The rails give with the weight of the train. These double decker trains are tall and if the rails give way and the train's going fast, it starts swaying from side to side and can go over."

He was indeed a retired railroad man, and his father had worked for the railroad before him. The two of them had ridden this way years ago, and the father had taught the boy many things. My retired railroad friend knew trains, and he knew this land and the history here. It was love. You could tell by the way he looked out the window as he talked, not at me, and by the way his words came effortlessly. He wasn't trying to convince me of anything or even to get my attention. He wasn't wishing I'd leave him alone, either. When you love something, there are times when you want to talk about it.

We were in North Dakota, and late in the morning we would be crossing into the long state of Montana.

So he told me. The train would spend the rest of the day going through Montana. I can't remember where my railroad friend was from, which was appropriate because his heart seemed to be with the prairie and not a particular place there, and also with the train itself, which, I was learning, is place as much as movement.

"How did your family get to the West?"

"My great-grandfather was a soldier in the Prussian army, and the railroad sent agents to Prussia to recruit homesteaders."

"Wait a minute," I said. I was thinking about what an effort it would have been for an American back then to travel across the Atlantic and into Prussia. "Why would the railroads have spent the money to go there and talk to people about homesteading?"

"They wanted this land settled," he said. "They wanted people who would grow crops and ship them to market by train and who would travel by train and buy things the train would bring." And, he added, the government wanted the railroad so it could get to the West Coast and to the silver mines of Nevada. So the government offered up the land.

"Why would a Prussian man want to come all this way?"

It had to be more than adventure. The Prussian man was going to have to settle and farm.

"A Prussian soldier had no opportunity to advance," he said. "Only aristocrats were officers, and only land-owners were aristocrats. Land was inherited. A soldier's children would have no opportunity either. So the offer of land was the draw."

My friend also knew the history of American railroads. He was the one to tell me that the *Empire Builder* was named after James J. Hill, whose nickname was the same. He told me some of the more modern history. Amtrak, the American passenger system, came into being under President Nixon. Of course passenger service had existed before, but it was privately owned. My friend knew not only the year, but also the date the transfer happened. Maybe he knew the time of day that the papers were signed. He knew who got the mail business and why that was important, and who controlled the tracks. If his information and my understanding were correct, freight controlled the tracks.

Several times on my long trip west and then again going back east, we slowed or even stopped for a time, and if the land was dry, and if an Amtrak person passed in the aisle and was asked why we were slowing, the answer was that we were letting a freight train go by. If that was true, and if these pauses were anticipated, then they had to be factored into the schedule. My friend commented that we were "making good time." Yesterday's train, he said, had been hours late to Seattle, "because of the flooding." There were times later that day when we went through water. We slowed way down then. You could put your forehead right up to the glass and look straight down and see nothing but water.

At first I was asking questions of my friend to keep things going, but gradually he began to get expansive, and Minot, in North Dakota, was the crossover in our conversation. "See that house?" he pointed out as we slowed for our stop. "See the line where the water peaked? Those cars, see over there? They look like they were flooded. They look like they're coated in mud."

"And those fields," he said, as we were traveling again. "That wheat's late. It should be higher. And that field hasn't been planted at all. Too wet." We watched the fields go by. "People love water," he said, "but water can be a bad thing." I was seeing his heart for the farmer.

He explained for me the geographical reason for the flooding in this particular place. This was no longer water from Devil's Lake. This water came from a river, which he named and I've forgotten, that originated in Canada, dropped down into the States, and then returned to Canada. Did I detect a little resentment towards Canada over the flooding? Maybe. It was hard to tell, and I didn't think to ask. He wasn't particularly demonstrative with his passions, and if he was resentful, as we all are from time to time, maybe there was reason behind it. Maybe Canada lacked the best flood control, as we did with Katrina, or maybe Canada had flood control that protected her but didn't mesh with ours. Maybe he was misinformed. Or maybe the resentment, if it was actually there, was just bias. No matter there, either. If he was biased, as we all are somewhere, then there was someone riding the train across Canada who was biased against the States. That's how people are. I have my biases—some I know about, certainly some that are subconscious. I was biased in his favor. I liked him.

I asked him where he was headed and he told me Seattle. From there he was taking another train to go south into California where he'd visit his son. After that, another train inland to visit another son. He would be traveling for weeks, he said, with obvious contentment.

"What a great way to travel," I said, looking out the window.

That's when he turned to me, that's when I got the real connection. "You know the Willie Nelson song?" I looked at him and nodded, though I didn't know. His face was composed. "That says it for me. 'The sons of Pullman porters, the sons of engineers, ride their father's magic carpet made of steam.'" He paused. We looked at each other. "This *is* my 'magic carpet made of steam.'"

"I get it," I said.

We didn't say much more. We had talked for hours. We watched out the window together.

I did know that song, after all. I recognized it immediately when he spoke the words. "City of New Orleans," recorded by Willie Nelson, by Arlo Guthrie, by many others, including Steve Goodman, who wrote it. It is one of the very best out of the wealth of good train songs.

After a time, I thanked him and went back to my seat. Carrie, my young seatmate, was gone, and I didn't see her again. She had surprised me earlier in the Observation Car when I was talking to my railroad friend. She had come up behind me and asked, in a quiet voice, if I knew where she could get a "pop," meaning a soft drink, and I'd told her how to get to the Snack Bar.

Anna Raglan

CHAPTER 14

It Is Like This

Sometime before leaving on the train trip, as I said, I made a list of things that worried me. I wrote them down in a notebook because I knew that I'd forget afterwards how I was thinking before.

The list was in no particular order except for the first thing. I knew without a doubt that wasting time was my biggest worry. Interesting. It doesn't seem logical, that being the biggest. In other words, I have no idea why that was so important.

Was it a personal problem? The way I felt pre-trip was like this: It seemed I was taking those three or four days, times two for the return trip, and tossing them into a black hole of wasted time. I am definitely not a workaholic, I can lounge with the best, but I can be terribly, terribly impatient. Was this my impatience looming large, a big monster?

Was this my culture? Does middle-class America try to make productivity a god? I think it does, sometimes, for better and for worse.

One of my heroes is Paul Salopek. Salopek is the journalist who wanted to walk the path of human migration. He left Ethiopia in January of 2013, walking, and the last I heard, as I write this chapter (winter, early 2015), he was in the country of Georgia. When he gets to the coast of Eastern Russia he will take a boat to Alaska, crossing what long ago was a land bridge, then continue his walk down North America and then South America to end up at the southern end of Chile. He estimates this journey will take him seven years. I love that—seven years. When asked why, he says, in the December 2013 issue of *National Geographic*, "for many reasons: to relearn the contours of our planet at the human pace of three miles an hour. To slow down." He goes on to list more, but it catches me that he has "go slow" in first place.

From my pre-trip notebook:

Fears about train trip

- *It will waste time*
- *Stations will be dangerous*
- *I won't be able to sleep*
- *I will get sweaty and greasy*
- *I will be confined*
- *I will be bored*
- *Everyone else will have iPhones and computers and I will be lonely.*

The fear of being bored (unspoken: "to death") was centered mostly on the entire day that I'd be on the train in the West. Wake up on the train, spend the day, go to sleep.

So far so good for that one. The best of conversations made the morning timeless. The rest of the day I did in blocks. Is it time to move? Is it time to sit? Left to my own devices, I would choose to sit, but I've had enough experience with depression to know that sometimes I need to prod myself into activity. I discovered that my car had a water dispenser. If I needed to move, I might take the cup I'd saved from the cranberry juice and walk to the dispenser which was by the narrow steps going to the lower level. I wanted to sip on water anyway, because of the dryness of air conditioning. On any walk through my car I'd see people, maybe exchange smiles, get to know the faces in the neighborhood.

Down the steps were the bathrooms. One of them had a separate fore room, with two sinks in a continuous counter and mirrors above. That was nice, nice for itself and also as part of a variety of spaces, of destinations. It was roomy, relatively speaking. Two could easily work at the same time. After the morning talk with my conductor friend, then a stop back at my seat for supplies, I headed for that counter room and did a slow hair-brushing and a slow face-washing. I had the room to myself.

Also downstairs was the vestibule, the little area where you entered or left the train. There were exit doors on either side, facing north, facing south, and the doors had windows, so you could stand there and look out at things from ground level. Things look different from ground level. You could have a conversation with someone else who wanted to stand awhile or you could enjoy being by yourself and standing for a change. Some people—not me, because I decided not to talk on the phone—went there to have private phone conversations. The stairs themselves were good for fitness sake, to get the blood moving. And nothing could beat the smoke stops, walking the platform, getting some air, seeing new things, new people. The smokers were always careful to go off by themselves, downwind.

At one of my sitting times I got my knitting out. I'd brought a half-finished red scarf in a lace pattern that I'd started long ago for my friend who died of cancer. Obviously, I didn't finish it in time for her. I'd put it away. I didn't remember doing this, but I may have tried once again to work on it because in its bag, a heavy plastic bag with a drawstring top, was a typed letter from an acquaintance who lived in New York City. She had written a group letter five days after 9/11. "It is good for us to gather together at times," she wrote of herself and her friends. "We don't feel like we have to talk much."

The red yarn had some mohair in it. Maybe I'll give the scarf to Nina, I thought, and wondered if red was fashionable or if mohair was. Gift anxiety.

Figuring out how to do the pattern again wasn't easy. It was the kind of project that I would have put off forever without the opportunity of a full day where time was, in a manner of speaking, free. Without this, the half a scarf would still be in its bag in the back of the least-used closet in the house, where I had made myself dig for it before the trip.

The pattern came from an old tattered booklet of hats and scarves, "Spinnovations 16," put out by the Spinnerin Yarn Co., Inc., probably from the seventies. Half of the pages were missing but not the one with the sincere-sounding missive and plea to us knitters to write if we were "ever in doubt" about any of the directions. We should "stop then and there" if we were in doubt, and start our letter. Spinnerin acknowledged that sometimes a mistake "slides by," and they apologized in advance, but they wanted to let us know that they couldn't be faulted for any "mis-interpretation" of the patterns.

I misinterpreted a lot. There is now a spot of chaos mid-scarf where I re-learned, and that's an advantage of choosing to knit a scarf. Mistakes are hidden when a scarf is in use, wound around a neck.

Knitting is not hard; it just takes time to learn. It might seem hard if you saw a pattern. Here is an example of mid-level knitting instructions: K2, *yo, K3, sl1, K1, psso, yo, K2tog, K2, yo, K1; rep from * end K2.

There was a huge stain on the bottom of the booklet, going through all twelve pages. It looked like burnt motor oil, but wasn't oily, and had, instead, turned the paper brittle. I asked Dee what he thought it was and he thought it was a burn, as I did at first, but it's an obvious stain if you look closely. I was a little embarrassed by it.

Eighteen photographs of individual models—men, women and children—wearing the finished hats and scarves showed knitters what they were supposed to be making. In five of the photos the models are acting wildly happy, and in thirteen they are acting serious, or, in the case of the adults, alluring.

My knitting needles probably dated from the sixties, and I had carted them, just about unused, through many moves. They were fourteen inches long, needlessly long for a scarf, and made of aluminum with a metallic light blue paint. Anyone who knitted in the sixties or seventies would know those needles and know the quiet metallic clicking they make when used. My mother, my sisters, and I would sometimes sit around on summer evenings back then and we would knit, not talking very much. My mother would have wanted to talk more, but we daughters could be sullen.

When I'd picked out my seat on the *Empire Builder*, still in the Chicago station, and lifted off my backpack, I was startled to discover that the knitting needles had poked their way through the plastic bag and then through the mesh of the backpack and were sticking out, weapon-like, all fourteen inches of them, held in only by the wider rim on the non-needle end. How long had they been that way?

For the very first leg of Paul Salopek's walk in Africa, he traveled with an Ethiopian guide and two camel drovers. They walked mostly through hot empty desert.

When they came upon people in villages or camps, and were asked "Where are you going?" Elema, the guide, would bend over laughing. "He enjoys the absurdity of it," Salopek writes. Salopek would then answer the question. "North. To Djibouti," he would say. He wouldn't talk about the whole plan, the walk to Chile. It would be "meaningless." Even a walk to the coast of Africa, to Djibouti, sounded insane to the African pastoralists they met. They obviously thought him crazy, or maybe physically ill and seeking a hospital. "Are you sick?" they would ask.

Salopek understood the reaction, and the reaction from those who did know the South American destination. He didn't start out on a whim. "To walk for seven years…Enduring hardship, loneliness, uncertainty, fear, exhaustion, confusion…"

I love that list! I don't have to write my own.

It's not just a list about a difficult journey. It's what goes with life.

And then there's this, again from Ethiopia. "On our best days we four ramblers recognize our immense good luck. We ricochet down steep mountain trails, almost running…bounce our voices off the walls of black-rock canyons in whooping contests…grin like children. The cameleers catch the spark, and sing.

"What is it like to walk through the world?

"It is like this. It is serious play. I will miss these men."

CHAPTER 15

The Neighborhood

A funny thing I noticed on the *Empire Builder*. Periodically, one of the passengers would announce, out of the blue, a personal calculation of the length of the trip in hours, from Chicago to Seattle. They'd say it with pride. They were performing, and wanted a tribe of those who agreed or, better yet, were impressed. I heard a few of these announcements, and I liked them. It was a benevolent whiff of the unexpected, like spotting a bright bird, like catching a brief fragrance of something pleasant on a walk, not necessarily something you need to name. Did the different estimates agree? I don't think so. I didn't pay attention to that. I still didn't care about the length of the trip. At this point, though, I was a convert. I was happy that I had a full day on the train. All mine. Nothing to worry about.

The majority of people in my car mostly sat and mostly were quiet. A few characters emerged, like the calculating people. There was a young man with remarkable conversational abilities. He was my diagonal. That means he sat across the aisle and one row ahead, in the aisle seat. That's the person you can notice the easiest. They can't see you unless they turn around. It's hard to look much at the person across from you, they'll catch you looking, and the seat backs are too high to see the people directly ahead of you or behind you.

My diagonal, the conversationalist, was a large person, not overweight, with a neat beard and an easy manner. I never noticed any impatience about him. He was maybe twenty-five. I'd first over-heard him speak not in his spot across from me, but in the Observation Car. His voice, which I heard before I saw him, was warm and easy, and his talk roamed widely, without lurching. World affairs, athletes, music, science, books. There was no aggression. He was interested in all things, not interested in winning, and not interested in an audience. His quiet attention was on the person he was talking to.

Directly in front of me were two girls, probably in their twenties as well. I found out they were from Germany when my diagonal started talking to them. The girls and I never spoke, but we always smiled at each other when I passed their seats. Maybe they saw me knitting, and I reminded them of family members back home. My mother says that Germans are very good knitters, very fast. Maybe the girls liked seeing an older woman traveling alone in this foreign place. Maybe I was reassuring. I warmed up my smile when I found out they were from Germany. I was glad they were visiting my country and the beautiful West, and that they were using the train. Few American girls would do that.

My diagonal the conversationalist had a seatmate, the flashier of the two in looks and manner, who started speaking to the girls in German. My diagonal joined in but Flashy had the better German—pretty good, really, to my ears—and I was a little sad about his superior showing because I was rooting for my diagonal. It didn't matter. The girls were self-contained. Though they seemed to enjoy the talk and were laughing, they did not seem interested in more. Overall, I was happy that any American could speak some German. I know no German. I know a little high school French, a tiny bit of Spanish, and two cocktail toasts that are distant linguistic relatives of Czechoslovakian. My father was in Czechoslovakia, in the American infantry, when World War II ended. I think there were celebrations.

In Montana, the *Empire Builder* stopped at stations about every hour, and a few people got on and off, mostly on. I would look out the window to see what the station was all about and paid no attention to the new people, until Birdie showed up. "Is this an oven or what?" That announcement of her presence and her displeasure was delivered from the top of the steep steps. I looked up, and I'm sure others did too. Birdie was surveying the seat situation. She was probably looking for an empty one, I guess we all do, and she was certainly recovering from the steps. She wasn't in the best of health, as we soon found out.

Birdie had dressed squarely on the comfortable side of the comfort v. looks question. Maybe that was part of her problem with the temperature in the car. She had chosen a sweatshirt and sweatpants, in the baggy style. She also wore a baseball cap turned backwards.

I myself never had a complaint about the air quality or temperature on any of my Amtrak trains. I liked having it cool at night, blanket temperature. Some people might never need a blanket, but I am cold-natured. At home, I sleep under three wool blankets in winter.

Birdie was a smoker. Like most, she knew when a smoke stop was coming. Some of the smokers would line up before the stop and Birdie was always there, at the head. There weren't enough smoke stops and they weren't long enough, she told us all, loudly, impatiently, during one wait. She was traveling west to see her doctor in Seattle. She complained about her home state. "It has nothing for me!" she declared, commenting on its inadequate medical offerings. Maybe that was an exaggeration born from all kinds of things, including frustration with being ill. I'm thankful for my good health. I was thankful for the smoke stops, too. Some had a particular entertainment, like ice cream for sale or restored old train engines to see. If you wanted conversation, there was usually one to be had.

Really, Birdie wasn't bad. She did not talk non-stop. She was more entertaining than obnoxious. Train riders are mostly OK. Quiet or pleasant or entertaining. When there are delays, there is a little tension, but most people handle it well.

Once in the Observation Car, a young man came up and took a seat near me, smiled a greeting, looked out the window for a bit, then asked me to watch his things, which you probably don't need to do on the *Empire Builder*. When he returned we talked a little, and then he called someone on his phone. He started his talk with a coldly delivered "Put your mother on the phone." That's it. No "Hello." Then he had a too-loud mean and condescending conversation with the mother, I guess his wife or ex-wife. The volume and rudeness seemed to be partly for my benefit. He'd look over and smile at me, as if we were comrades. He was troubled and trying to spread trouble. I hope he and those in his world have found some peace. That interchange stood out only because it was so unusual. All in all, I came away with an upbeat and immensely reassuring view of America and the people who ride trains.

Earlier in the day, when I was leaving the Observation Car after my talk with the retired conductor, I saw and picked up a discarded newspaper and read about the last-minute debt limit deal. No one liked it apparently, but the deal was made, the government would keep working, the *Empire Builder* would ride on to Seattle.

I also read, at intervals during the day, the book I had chosen to bring with me. It was the perfect book.

CHAPTER 16

A Faith In Books

I'd made the list of worries before I left, but I didn't bother to make a list of what I thought would be easy. There were only two of those, after all—the familiar station in Washington, DC and plenty of time to read. Choosing what to bring to read was a pleasure. I have a faith in books, a solid faith that the right book shows up at the right time.

It wouldn't be fiction. I can be hard on fiction. I didn't want to risk taking a book, a companion, that would get on my nerves, adding to the possible or probable physical discomforts. And be this trip good or bad, I wanted to experience it. I didn't want to get lost in someone's fictional world. There's a time for that, but this wasn't the time.

I also decided to take just one book. I wanted to make myself hear what one author said on one subject, to give one author a real chance, not let myself be tempted to flit from one book to another.

I found the right one surprisingly quickly, in a catalogue. It was a book about the "reinvention" of knowledge, telling the changing, evolving story of what humans know, against the backdrop of human history. What is being figured out, paired with what is happening. Perfect, I thought. I cross America by train and travel the history of human knowledge by book. When the book arrived I let myself read the back cover but not the flyleaf or anything else. I put it on top of a pile of books on a decrepit dresser at the bottom of the basement stairs. I would remember where it was. I could see it when I went down to do laundry.

This is good, I thought about my choice. I am happy and will check this item off the list.

But no. I worried. Here is one of my many worried entries from the notebook I kept pre-trip:

July 2, 2011
In advance of reading a book about knowledge, I try to think of what I can say I know. I give up because I feel my head starting to hurt, then I try again, then give up again, and then think about something I read that a physicist said, I think Brian Greene. "Neither philosophy nor science can prove that the world exists." So I don't think we can know anything. We can only believe.

Reinventing belief? I guess people do that all the time.

I believe, sorta, that knowledge will come from within, as in "self-evident." All of us are equal. We are free. We have everything we need.

Things like that.

What about food? I'm afraid if I take a lot of food, I'll just eat it all the first day, out of boredom. I know I would.

"*I don't think we can know anything,*" I write, and then I go on to talk about what we might be able to know. First draft.

But suffice it to say, I worried a lot.

Who gets to decide what is knowledge? I worried about that.

The book of knowledge didn't stay perfect for long. I churned about the decision, then, finally, took the book from its pile and shelved it. I'd read it some other time. For the trip, it was too risky.

Now what? I wasn't anxious. I still had faith. I thought about a travel book. No, too much like what I was doing. A biography. No, too focused. History? Maybe.

Most book lovers have books they've never read, but intend to read, and in the end the perfect book was right in front of me. It was in another pile of books on another broken-down dresser in the basement. The book cover was familiar. I'd moved it many times during the course of many basement clean-ups and re-shufflings. The cover had a utilitarian design that made me think it started out on someone's college course list. I don't remember getting it. I probably bought it at a used book sale. It was categorized on the back as "Current Affairs," and was published in 1997. I didn't understand the title, *The Warrior's Honor,* and that was a draw, but it was also the kind of thoughtful-looking book I'd probably never give an honest chance unless I was sequestered somewhere. That was the kind I wanted.

It remained the choice, and I went on to other things, fine-tuning the decisions on clothing and other necessities. On the calm sunny day of packing and leaving, when Dee and I were headed to the truck, I make a last-minute change of plans and dashed back into the house, frantically searched for and then found a second book. I would take a second after all, a travel book, a book I'd already read, Paul Theroux's *Iron Rooster.* Just in case.

Inside the back cover of *Warrior's Honor* is a paragraph about author Michael Ignatieff, describing him as a "writer, historian, and television producer." During the 1990s he traveled to the places in the world where ethnic conflict was the worst—Bosnia, central Africa, Afghanistan, Ireland, and others—looking to understand the hatred and brutality. In this collection of essays he reports what he saw and came to believe.

Ignatieff first gives historical background, starting with the empire building of the 1800s. Wealthy nations and companies went looking for treasure in the undeveloped countries. Years later, after World War II, the ideology of the Cold War added fuel to the competition that had developed among nations. Then, in the 1990s, a "narrative of compassion" developed, one that impelled the "zones of safety" to make the zones of danger their business. "Western nations made attempts unprecedented in scope to help out in areas of conflict." They sent medical aid and food, monitored elections, tried to protect at least some minority populations, worked to bring warring sides to mediation. Ignatieff emphasizes the change that this type of action implied. "We are scarcely aware of the extent to which our moral imagination has been transformed since 1945 by the growth of a language and practice of moral universalism, expressed above all in a shared human rights culture."

Does intervention help? That seems to be the question Ignatieff wanted to answer. He says that "almost everyone" who goes to help has wondered at times if they are making things worse, more chaotic, more violent.

It is clear, educated, thoughtful writing. Ignatieff packs the first essay with philosophical argument, plenty to chew on, and I wanted some of that. "...the Marxist tradition has always regarded bourgeois moral universalism as a veil of ideological deception." Interesting. I wasn't sure what it meant or whether I cared. This was a new way of thinking for me and unfamiliar vocabulary, so the going was slow in that introductory essay, and I was glad I was free to get up and check out what was happening in the Observation Car.

My other book, *The Iron Rooster*, tells of author Paul Theroux's travels by train in China in the 1980s. I'd read it years ago and remembered a few things clearly. Cities had lots of small and interesting parks, and groups of people used them for Tai Chi, or dance, or to practice foreign languages, the parks a sign of a healthy community spirit.

Two, there were Chinese young people who liked having English nicknames; some had them already and some asked Theroux to give them a name.

And, three, on the trains, an attendant would come around with thermos bottles of hot water so you could make your tea; a cultured and hospitable tradition, I thought.

I made a quick decision to take this particular book as a back-up because I vaguely remembered a certain other tradition. On a train in a rural area, I thought I remembered, Theroux saw someone spit on the floor. Maybe more than one someone.

If I was miserable during the trip, my reasoning went, I could spend some of the miserable time looking for the part in the book where someone spit on the floor. I didn't think anyone on my trains would be spitting. It wouldn't be that bad.

CHAPTER 17

We Are Here Together

I am reading right now (April 2015) a book called *Grieving*. I saw it in the *Chinaberry* book catalogue, one that I trust. Grieving is something I should know about, I thought, and I ordered it, by mail. My letter had to cross the country to California, home of the *Chinaberry* group, and a week after I'd sent my order they called me and said they'd sold out and they weren't going to re-stock it. The next time I was in my local bookstore I asked them to order it. They did. It took a while for the book to arrive and then another week for me to pick it up.

When I paid for the book, I glanced at the cover and thought, No way I want to read a book about grieving. I put it in a pile in the basement.

That was a few months ago. Then a friend of mine went through a tough break-up, and I thought I'd dig it out and coach myself to try to be helpful, in a truly helpful way.

Author Jerusha Hull McCormack has lived in the United States and also in Dublin, a mecca for the literary. Her husband died when their two sons were young. She is honest, and she can write.

Grieving was indeed helpful. Show up, McCormack advises. Be present. Listen, but only when you have the time and attention to do so. Bring food, invite your friend on a walk, don't try to "fix" the pain, and don't say too much. There is reward for you both, she says, which I was surprised to read, and the reward is peace.

The book was written primarily, of course, for someone who is grieving. It's personal, though not a diary. In fact, McCormack stays at a distance, but her writing and her experiences are both so real and deep that the result is sometimes mysterious, beckoning. The "encounter with sorrow," she says, does not have to stay with loss alone. "For, liberated from the old, shop-worn clichés, grieving may become another kind of occurrence altogether: a voyage out to the limits of one's known world."

I liked that she had a fierce side. She was impatient with the stereotyping of widowhood. "You do not have to live up to the expectations of others. You have done nothing wrong. Why should you do penance? Why should you be treated as a nuisance or a threat?" I thought her observations astute. "The modern Western world is a cruel one for grieving." All around is the worship of success, progress, acquisition, independence, permanence. How does one grieve in that world?

By slowing down, for one. Sometimes that slower pace is not by choice. Grief can slow you down. In that vein,

McCormack highlights the place that poetry can hold in difficult times, and includes a range of poems. The design of the book sets these off from her writing in a respectful way. I haven't read poetry in years, so consider the source, but I thought the poems she chose do the things poems do best. There is space enough to breathe—to find something of oneself that is quiet, yet solid. Something discovered alone, yet understood to be shared.

I liked her conclusions. It takes courage to choose to live, she says, to resist the many ways we have to numb ourselves. And the surprising "reorientation," as she calls it, fiercely rejecting the idea of recovery, is the discovery that "everything is connected," and to a degree previously unimaginable. Love has no limits. "When you become comfortable with uncertainty, infinite possibilities open up in your life."

Westbound on the *Empire Builder,* I met the other side of Westward expansion. I met a Native American man. He was a type like my train-pro friend Allison—the effortlessly kind and intelligent type. He was "present," "real." How does someone get to be that way? Get to be wise? Perhaps someone else had been "present" for him. If this man ever had trouble, and of course he did, trouble being part of the human condition, someone had been there for him, and he'd paid attention. If he'd ever had to mourn the loss of his ancestors' way of life, somebody had helped him. If forgiveness is the key to happiness, he had given forgiveness a try.

He was riding with us as a storyteller. He gave a program mid-afternoon in the Observation Car, but by the time I got there it was so crowded that I went back to my seat. I went again later and saw him talking alone to two other passengers, and I joined them, and then the other two left.

He was an older man, tall with broad shoulders, and he wore Native ceremonial dress. He was the wise elder, though we were probably about the same age, and I was the essentially silly student. I asked chattery questions, and he gave relaxed and thoughtful answers. We talked of many things.

I mentioned the small lakes that had surprised me, and he told me of working with horses, training them by leading or riding them into a lake like the ones we had passed. The water would be calming to the horse. I'd been a horse-crazy kid, doing most of my riding in my imagination, and as we talked I saw myself in my mind's eye, riding the wild one, riding the one no one else could handle, right into the water. His children really did ride those horses into the water. He'd taught them horses. He had two boys and a girl, as I remember. They were grown by then, all serving in the military. I'd bet they are good leaders.

He taught me, and it took him many attempts, how to say the name of the woman most of us Eastern Americans know as Sacajawea. That is inaccurate, he said. What is inaccurate, I wonder now. The name itself? The spelling? Just the pronunciation? I don't remember,

Anna Raglan

and I don't remember how to say her name as he taught me. If I saw him now, I would find pen and paper and write it phonetically. I would write his name, too, which I can't remember either.

He had a calming presence, like calm water. Being with him was, at the same time, energizing, as if he had learned to appreciate the beauty of who he was, the world he was born into, and the present moment. And it was as if that appreciation were catching.

When our time was up, I wanted to remember him and the way he was dressed. I asked if I could take his picture, and I cringed immediately, remembering the stereotypes of people taking pictures of Native Americans in the tourist towns. But he was exceedingly gracious. He was used to this and did not let my request bother him. "Let's get someone to take our picture together," he said, without any reference to any mistake, and we did. He was a teacher.

I love the outdoors. I'm not Native American, but if I were, I'd surely have to grieve over the loss of the land. I'm thankful for historians who have written about the mistreatment of those who were here first. Not that attention equals guilt. It doesn't. Making amends is a different subject altogether, but guilt is certainly not helpful; it paralyses. Or just as bad, it generates other unhappy thoughts, like anger or anxiety, or depression, or defensiveness, to cover the guilt. I think the replacement of the hunter/gatherer/nomadic world by agriculture was inevitable, but of course the change could have been made much more humanely, more slowly. Greed and fear got in the way, as it so often does. But who am I to point at greedy people? I can be plenty greedy.

And who am I to be self-righteous? My ideas about empire building needed an adjustment, too. McCormack, in *Grieving*, reminds us of suttee, the practice of a widow throwing herself on her husband's funeral pyre, outlawed by the British in India. That was progress. Historian Yuval Noah Harari says that volumes could be written, and have been, on the good effects of European empire building and volumes on the bad effects of the same. Interesting.

A friend back home, not Native, spent a weekend on a Native American spirituality retreat. This was his wife's idea. One of the things he did on the retreat was to help build and use a sweat lodge. To my friend's relief and surprise, the weekend was a good experience. He was changed, or so he said, at least a little.

Journalist Brooke Randle recently interviewed Bruce Akitchitay Carlino, who is of Cherokee and Taino ancestry, and who leads and sits "in ceremony" with others in a sweat lodge. He does this in his spare time and doesn't care about the race or ethnicity of those who sit with him. He cares if people are "honorable," if they are willing to recognize the spiritual aspect of the experience. He is grateful to have had this in his life, to have learned among his elders, to feel the depth of the practice, to be able to offer this to others, some who come his way "in dire straits," he says. He believes that we all need help at times, and he is glad that he can offer help.

I did work with some guilt when remembering my conversation with the storyteller, especially over forgetting his name. I didn't even ask his tribe. I didn't think of asking. Was he Sioux? Crow? Ojibwe? An image of him came to help me in my guilt. I saw him standing out on a rise, in the open Western lands, at peace and looking far into the distance. I would like to be more like him.

If a strong man is at home on the wide spaces of the prairie, comfortable with solitude, comfortable with people, and if he has within him the life of the old stories born of that place, then he will want to tell those stories. He is wise enough to know that some people can't hear them yet, but that will not affect the joy of telling, because he tells them at the right time and because the stories are life themselves. To tell them is to revisit. And some people will be able to hear.

CHAPTER 18

My Generation

The seat behind the seat of my across-the-aisle neighbor Air Force Hat was turned backwards and the seat behind that seat was faced forwards, making a place for a party of four to the back of me.

Somewhere in the full day on the westbound *Empire Builder*, a young girl and her little brother got on alone and were taken to that place by the attendant for our car. Our attendant was a small Asian woman. She'd stop by from time to time and sit across from the sister and brother who were in the forward facing seat, and talk with them. The attendant was sincerely friendly and naturally cheerful, not pushy. She was the kind of person most young people would trust.

"What do you want to be when you grow up?" she asked them.

They knew exactly. The little girl wanted to be a movie star and her little brother wanted to be a football player. To that, the attendant responded with suitable or maybe diplomatic appreciation and then moved the talk into a warm and reassuring inter-generational discussion of dreams and, with emphasis, the importance of doing well in school. The kids weren't that impressed with the school part, it seemed, but I was. Nice touch, I thought. Good family stuff.

At one of the longer stops, for refueling, the attendant and I talked outside on the platform and I found out she was from the Philippines, from Manila. Her name was Adelina.

I told her I remembered when the computer operators in Manila walked out during an election after they were told by the party in power to falsify data. This occurred during one of the periods in my life when I paid decent attention to the news, and I had thought the walk-out really great, and courageous of course. The party in power was headed by a dictator.

Adelina's face clouded as soon as I mentioned "election."

"I never go to Manila during elections."

"Tense?" I asked.

"And violent," she said.

Her smile returned. "But the hospitality, the hospitality there. That is what is so good."

I once saw on a friend's shelf a book titled *Mean People*. I couldn't resist. The author was a world traveler, as well as a self-proclaimed expert on people, and he firmly believed that Filipinos were the world's friendliest people. That's quite an accolade!

Why do people behave the way they do?

This is what Michael Ignatieff set out to answer, in the realm of conflicts that make world news. He came to believe this: "There is nothing in our nature that makes ethnic or racial conflict unavoidable." He says that one variable is the stability, or lack of, in the state.

"'Authoritarian' is not the same as 'stable,'" says Paul Theroux.

Outside the window, as we rolled along during the afternoon, was beautiful Montana in its reassuring sameness. About once an hour we'd stop at a station in a town, but mostly we saw just land. Every now and then we'd pass a little house sitting all by itself a ways away, on top of a ridge, or half-way up a hill facing us. Were these old homesteader cabins? Did the Ingalls family ever live in Montana?

When I went to the Observation Car, going from car to car, I practiced train-pro Allison's smooth way of opening the doors. Maybe I improved. It wasn't as easy as it looked, for me. I never got another seat mate. I spread out my things, and sometimes I put everything but my pillow on the floor at my feet and lay crossways. I always had my head to the window and my feet to the aisle, until I saw on a walk someone doing the other way, head to the aisle, feet to the window. That took some nerve, because your head, on the arm rest, sticks out a little into the aisle. But anything for a change, and I tried it. What would make me more comfortable? That was a frequent question. I put on my cardigan, took it off, put on socks, took off socks, changed from my shoes to my plastic sandals and back again. Seeking maximum comfort was a pleasant way to move just a little, and pass some time.

I had another eight-thirty dinner reservation. When it was called and I got up to go, my neighbor Air Force Hat got up too, and we got to the Dining Car at the same time and were seated at the same table. There was another man already seated, his name turned out to be Mark, and my neighbor, who turned out to be named Rock, sat beside him, and I sat opposite the two. We started to get to know one another, exchanging the particulars, and I was thinking that this was going to be a fun dinner. Our waiter, tall and confident, friendly, came by and asked if we wanted drinks. Rock and I each ordered a glass of Cabernet, and Mark passed. This worried me. Maybe Mark wasn't a drinker and would look down on us for drinking, and the friendship we seemed to have started would end. Did he sense my worry? He told us he'd had his glass of wine at his seat before coming to dinner. So this was going to work out. And, I noted to myself, that's another way to pass some time. Have a drink in the seat before going to dinner. But no, I countered, you'd want a second with dinner and that's not good for you. Our wine arrived and we toasted "Cheers!"—Mark with his water.

I thought we were near the same age and I told mine because few men in my generation are going to ask a woman her age. I was right, we were the same age, and I was the oldest. I was fifty-nine, Rock was fifty-eight, and Mark was the baby, fifty-seven. I was feeling supremely happy about all of us being the same age when our waiter's confident voice sounded behind me, speaking to us, speaking from the direction of the entrance to the Dining Car. "I've brought you a fourth."

I looked over my shoulder and saw Birdie. Oh, no.

Birdie took, in an announcing, flouncing way, the empty seat beside me as I scooted across the bench towards the window. We all greeted each other.

We went around again with names, which was how I learned hers. We skipped asking her age, maybe because nobody thought of it, maybe because she looked about our age and that was good enough, but also because she jumped right in telling us that she *had* to eat often and on a regular schedule because of her health problems. Then she told us all the problems she either had or was being tested for, and it was a lengthier list than most people could have come up with if they'd had to name every health problem they could think of. We three looked at her as she named, being good listeners, I think. Or maybe we were dazed. Maybe we stared.

Birdie was proud of her list, and that's not necessarily a bad thing. You have all of these problems and possible problems, and yet you are up and going and traveling on a train and making friends. It's impressive, when you think about it. She got near the end of her naming, slowed down, dredged up another one or two that she had left out, then seemed satisfied. She nodded to herself and looked around at us and smiled. We looked back.

"But I'm not contagious!" she burst out with a laugh, and we suddenly remembered where we were, smiled, and nodded our appreciation of that fact and all the rest.

Our handsome waiter came by again to bring us the menus and to tell us about the specials and to offer Birdie a drink. We took our menus, she declined the drink, and he left.

We all then looked at our menus in silence, an uncomfortable silence for me because everything had changed so with Birdie's arrival and I hadn't settled with the change. The silence didn't last long. Maybe Birdie didn't like silence or maybe a menu made her anxious. She put hers down and started telling us about her dogs, how much she missed them, and she pulled out a Smart Phone to show us pictures. This was the only Smart Phone I remember seeing on the train. I didn't mind the pictures. In fact, all of us, including Birdie, relaxed with the pictures and the dogs. You could tell that she really loved them, and I'd already decided what to order anyway.

Our waiter soon returned, took his expectant position with order pad in hand and looked at Birdie. We all reflexively picked up our menus again and studied them, or pretended to, and Birdie scowled.

Silence.

"Don't you have anything gluten-free?" she finally asked.

I had wondered about that myself. In 2011, "gluten-free" had barely made it to the Southeast, but I had two relatives on the West Coast who'd been diagnosed gluten intolerant, and the topic had come up when family gatherings were discussed. I had read the menu with that in mind, out of curiosity, and had been surprised to see no mention of gluten. The menus looked as if they were standard for all of Amtrak, and some of the more celebrated routes are in California.

"Everything except the pasta is gluten-free," he said.

Birdie continued to scowl and stare at her menu. The happiness of living with dogs was forgotten. Our waiter stood and looked calmly at her, then, after a considerate wait, said he'd give us a little more time. He left. Professionally done, I thought.

The frown stayed, then Birdie suddenly put her menu down with an added look of disgust and said she was feeling ill and that she wouldn't be able to eat anything they had anyway, and she got up and left us and we watched her go.

We didn't know what to do, or at least I didn't. I looked back at the menu. Our waiter returned.

"Where'd your friend go?" he asked.

We told him she'd decided not to eat dinner.

The very professional waiter barked out a laugh. "Well I guess *you're* not sorry!" We three, I hate to tell you, barked our laughs in return. Tension gone again.

But only for a second. I looked right back at the menu. I felt so guilty, so mean, so undeserving of my health, so disrespectful of a sister, all of that, and probably more.

Silence again.

Then Rock spoke. I only heard him. I was looking at my menu. "And we wish her well," he said to our waiter, for us all.

That was it. Nothing about the entire trip was any better. It may have been the best thing.

I ordered the pork chops. They might have been a little dry. That was fine. I gave up trying to cook pork chops long ago because they always turned out dry for me. I don't usually even order them. By far, most of the food I ate on the train was very, very good, and I appreciated every single thing about the Dining Car. Regardless, this particular meal was without a doubt my favorite of all the meals I ate on the train, because it was my generation, because it was two fun people, and because the wine was nice. We had a great time talking about all kinds of things. I loved it. My generation. Thank you, Rock, brother. Thank you, thank you.

CHAPTER 19

The Rewards Of Small Deeds

My favorite of the essays in the book I brought to read was "The Warrior's Honor," the one author Ignatieff used for the title of the whole collection. It must have been his favorite, too. It's about the International Red Cross.

When we Americans think of the Red Cross, most of us are thinking of the American Red Cross, of blood drives and disaster relief, those wonderful acts of assistance. The International Red Cross came first, and has a different purpose. It was born on one man's vacation to Italy.

In June, 1859, Swiss traveler Jean-Henri Dunant watched from an Italian hillside the battle of Solferino, between the French and Austrian armies. The fighting lasted an entire day. "At dusk, the emperor of Austria abandoned the field, and his troops streamed away in defeat." Dunant went down to the battlefield and saw the horrors you can imagine, including wounded men who had been left on their own to survive or die.

Afterward, in the hill town of Castiglione above the battlefield, Dunant found thousands of other wounded soldiers of both armies, lying "side by side in the churches, squares and lanes of the village." He stayed for days, doing his best to tend to the wounded and to help organize the nursing efforts of the villagers. Then he left, returned home, wrote a book, and re-directed his life.

Ignatieff: "For most liberal Europeans, Solferino was a glorious victory that helped to secure the eventual freedom of Italy from the Austrians. For Dunant, Solferino was a moral puzzle he was to struggle to decipher all his life, and the neglect of the wounded a scandal that gave the lie to myths of a nation's gratitude to its soldiers."

The book Dunant wrote about this moral puzzle made him famous and opened eyes, and the Swiss-based International Red Cross came into being, dedicated to the idea that attempts must be made to mitigate the horror of war. Soon after, this group drafted what we know as the Geneva Convention, which set into words the belief, among others, that enemy wounded deserve care equal to one's own.

"To be fair," Ignatieff tells us, "Dunant himself never believed in the authority of an international convention alone. Without ever arguing the point he understood that such conventions drew upon a deeper moral source—the codes of a warrior's honor." Warrior codes have existed in most, if not all, cultures, and though they vary, all proclaim the principles of fighting fair and protecting non-combatants. These codes, in their original form, were "particularist." They didn't apply to all people. The Christian code of chivalry, to use Ignatieff's example, did not apply to non-Christians, and the Christian warrior could do what he wanted to heretics or non-believers. One of the aims of the Geneva Convention was to craft a universal code.

The International Red Cross, officially known as the International Committee of the Red Cross, or ICRC, did not work to end war, but to make war more humane. This could be controversial, even within the organization. To be neutral you have to bypass the labels "aggressor" and "victim." Ignatieff's essay is stronger because he himself came to the subject from an "anti-war culture," as he puts it.

Neutrality for the ICRC was vital, and staunchly upheld. This hard-won position earned invaluable trust and access, and also made for dangerous work. Some warriors don't understand or don't respect neutrality. In the middle of the night of December 17, 1996, a group of masked men climbed the walls surrounding a Red Cross hospital in Chechnya and murdered six workers in their beds. Neutrality exposes one to danger, certainly, but in 1997, the year Ignatieff did much of his work and published his book, there were more applicants to the organization than open positions.

"So what are you here to escape?"

This was an interview question, the first asked of an ICRC applicant who talked to Ignatieff about the application process. Ignatieff goes on to list some answers, presumably ones he heard from delegates, as members are called. "Sometimes it is a failed marriage, the claustrophobic security of Swiss life, or the featureless grind of a modern career." Delegates in 1997 came from all over the world. Most wanted to make a difference. Some got worn down and left. Others stayed, at times sustained by "the rewards of small deeds," at times working hard to balance "cynicism and commitment."

In late 1996, Ignatieff visited a Taliban prison in the recently Taliban-seized capital of Afghanistan, Kabul, accompanying an ICRC delegate. The cell he described, "approximately six feet by ten feet," held eighteen former government militia recruits, mostly teenagers, "squatting on dirty mattresses. A few plastic bags of belongings hung from nails on the walls. The smell of the cell was animal-close but clean."

The delegate took information from each prisoner in turn, filled out an identification card, and gave it back to the prisoner. "Many received their cards with a little bow or with the Afghan gesture of placing a hand briefly over the heart." If nothing else, the visit from a foreigner was a thin tonic for loneliness and fear, proof that someone remembered. A few of the prisoners wanted to tell their stories, specifically of

Taliban promises of amnesty, but the ICRC delegate was unconcerned. He was there to see that they were treated decently and were registered, registration that might prevent a disappearance. The unconcern with stories of possible injustice was not received happily. "Dark looks were exchanged, and there was a lot of clicking of tongues as we bowed and made our way out through the cell door." But this is what neutrality can do. It can give access to a Taliban prison.

CHAPTER 20

We The People

The second night on the *Empire Builder* passed uneventfully and in relative luxury because I kept my own seat. Maybe I was awake more than asleep but I didn't stress about it. I was more relaxed. I'd dozed off some during the day before anyway.

I once read a book by an American anthropologist who went to live with an Amazon tribe. Everyone slept in hammocks in a big circle around the central community area. Sometimes during the middle of the night someone would get up and make a speech from the center. I assume there were tribal rules about the speeches, but none that the anthropologist mentioned.

In the early morning while it was still dark, Rock called over quietly from across the aisle and asked if I was going to breakfast, and I said yes and we went, no reservation required. We goofed and missed the time change and showed up an hour before breakfast started, which was funny to us. We returned an hour later and were seated with a woman our age who lived on a ranch in Arizona and an elderly man. This was a Wednesday, and I ordered my first coffee since Friday. Four days without coffee. This was the day for getting to Seattle.

The elderly gentleman was probably the oldest person on the train and certainly the best dressed. He wore a coat and tie, the coat classically refined, of a conservative checked material, the tie a bow tie. His shirt was pin-striped, his eye glasses had narrow tortoise-shell rims, and his white hair was neatly trimmed and neatly combed. His was the picture perfect Ivy League fashion of a nearly bygone era. He had indeed attended an Ivy League school. He told of riding the train to college from his home in the Deep South, and flirting with the wealthy girls going to Smith and Wellesley. He had not grown up wealthy. His father had been a professor.

Our Ivy League man went on to a career in the Foreign Service under LBJ, President Johnson. I'm assuming he had been capable and hard-working. I think if you worked for Johnson you had to be. Johnson was known for hard work and long hours and for expecting the same of others. At one time during his career, our breakfast companion found himself in a position that required more than he wanted to give. He spent months looking for the right replacement. He told us that Johnson would have given him "holy hell" if he'd found someone ever deemed substandard.

Prior to being president, Johnson had been a powerful leader in the Senate. So we heard. "His way was this:

He would put his arm around you and tell you that you were the greatest man he'd ever met. He meant it and you believed him. The trouble was, five minutes later, he would have forgotten all that and would be calling you a son of a bitch. It worked in the Senate."

I love President Johnson. I know, I know….Vietnam. I don't know what to say about Vietnam, except that I believe Johnson agonized about it. Civil Rights is why I love him. I think he was the person who, being among other things a Southerner, could give the necessary presidential push for the magnificent Civil Rights legislation of the sixties—the Civil Rights Act of 1964 and the Voting Rights Act of 1965.

The Civil Rights Act desegregated the hotels, restaurants, busses, movie theatres, trains and who knows what else in the South. A White restaurant owner could no longer say, "We don't serve Blacks." It ended the horrible "Whites Only" signs.

But in the rural South, Black people were still kept from voting. They were blocked in some places from simply entering the courthouse. They might be subjected to poll taxes and to deliberately impossible qualifying tests. They might be threatened if they spoke about registering. They might be fired from jobs, beaten up, and even murdered if they did manage to register. There were some sympathetic White people, but the vocal ones were few and were criticized or vilified by other Whites. Everyone who resisted obviously did so with courage. Black leaders pressed Johnson for a law to protect the right to vote, but he refused. We can't get it done now, he said. Too much, too soon. It won't go through Congress. This was certainly true.

It was equally true that some Black Southerners, and a few others, could not sit patiently and wait under such oppression. They felt compelled to act. To their immense and eternal credit, showing a depth of faith in humanity that seems rare, or at least a willingness to acquiesce to those with faith, they continued to act non-violently. They protested non-violently. And then, Selma.

Television captured the violence against the protestors in images that shocked the world. Johnson spoke to the nation, on TV. This is a problem for all of us, he said, this "crippling legacy of bigotry and injustice." Even then, it took intense grassroots pressure, Congressional support from both parties, and a Southern Democrat president willing to challenge the powerful segregationist Southern Democrat senators to get the Voting Rights Act passed. And Johnson had to have known he was handing over the South to the Republicans.

Our breakfast companion was stationed in Ethiopia when Selma happened. I'm grateful that America had such an intelligent, considerate, hard-working, equality-minded man in an African country during that time of intense turmoil in American race relations.

Selma was international news. Prince Philip, we were told, visited Ethiopia around that time, and gave some of the more defensive, less informed White Southerners on the staff a bit of a ribbing, but not so they noticed. "You know Prince Philip," our friend said.

I asked and heard about Ethiopia itself, and its history. I jotted down notes when I got back to my seat. Ethiopia was Christianized by missionaries from Constantinople in the 4th century. There was something about "the son of Vasco de Gama" and about "when the other African countries rose up against Portugal, Ethiopia refused to join them." When our friend first moved there in the 1960s, "the emperor and the nobility and the church owned all the land, and the peasants lived their lives."

"What church?" I asked.

"Coptic."

Our friend then told us a story from the seventies, an "unsavory tale," from the time of the 1974 military take-over. There was in Ethiopia then a certain American member of a certain American clandestine group, who ended up, during the chaos of the take-over, with a substantial amount of Ethiopian gold, all at one time. Then, in short order, newly wealthy, this man quit his job, divorced his wife, moved to South America, and married "what the French call 'an expensive princess.'" Our Foreign Service friend saw this happen and contacted a higher-up in the clandestine group. Unfortunately, there was not enough evidence. Nothing could be done.

I was a rapt audience for everything, and certainly the "unsavory tale." Our friend noticed this and laughed, thinking back over that last part, his conversation with the higher-up. "He'd probably seen a lot worse." The moral, our story-teller concluded, was this: "If you do dirty tricks for your country, you can easily spill over and do dirty tricks for yourself."

I'd called him elderly, but that can be a misleading word. There was nothing old about him. He didn't even move old. He told us lots of stories, but only because we'd asked, or I had. It was mostly me. He wasn't stuck on himself. That's what I liked best about him.

Here is what author Robert Coles has to say about Lyndon Johnson. He was "a restless, extravagantly self-centered, brutishly expansive, manipulative, teasing and sly man, but he was also genuinely, passionately interested in making life easier and more honorable for millions of hard-pressed working-class men and women. His almost manic vitality was purposefully, intelligently, compassionately used. He could turn mean and sour, but…he had a lot more than himself and his place in history on his mind."

This quote comes from *A History of Us,* Joy Hakim's American history series for young people, one of my favorite possessions and my source for much of what I have written about the Civil Rights years.

After we finished our breakfast, Rock, the woman from Arizona, and I were given tickets for our meals, and we each paid, but our Ivy League companion had a sleeper and his breakfast was included. He and the wait staff knew each other and were friendly. As we all got up to leave, I saw him put a ten-dollar bill down on the table. So that's how you do it, I thought. That's how you travel alone when you are advanced in years. You are kind and generous with the workers. You do your part to make their jobs pleasant, and they look out for you.

Soon after I got back to my seat, an attendant came through telling us that a number of passengers were joining us and we'd have to clear the way for seatmates. I'm a spread-out kind of person. I tidied up, enough to be cooperative, not enough to be the most inviting person on the train. Somewhat calculating, I have to admit. Sort of dirty trickish. Ah, well. I had most of my things on the floor all on my side, but some things beside me, some extending a few inches into the aisle seat, maybe enough to sow a touch of doubt in someone looking for a place. Birdie, up ahead in the car, told the attendant that she couldn't share a seat. We all heard her. "I have a contagious disease!" she said, loudly, with finality.

Rock hadn't brought anything in the way of carry-on, so his extra seat was invitingly empty. A woman joined him and set up her laptop. Rock went forward to sit in our old friend Mark's still lone seat, while Mark went to breakfast.

A volunteer with the National Park Service talked to us over the intercom, telling us about the Cascade Mountains and the engineering attempts to cross them. We heard of the great engineer Stevens, who directed the first complete tunnel and later worked on the Panama Canal, and of the current eight-mile New Cascade Tunnel, the longest tunnel in the US, which we passed through. We heard about the glaciers in Glacier National Park. In 2011 there were twenty-five. During the Civil War, there were one hundred and fifty.

I worked on my breakfast notes. I heard only the German girls talking to each other and the sound of the air circulation system and some very low train movement sounds. There was no clackety-clack, I suppose because we were on the upper level.

CHAPTER 21

Seattle

When I got back home after the trip, I thought about finding a book on Ethiopia. I tried two, but they weren't right, and I gave up. I did review Selma and the Civil Rights years. I already had those books.

"...the arc of the moral universe is long," said the Reverend Dr. King, "but it bends toward justice."

We were due to get into Seattle around 11 a.m. If a train attendant walked through the car, he or she was invariably asked by someone, "How's our time?" We were doing pretty well, it seemed, not like the train of the day before. "Maybe 10:55," said one attendant, "if they give us all green lights." I did my usual, knitted or read or watched out the window, listened to the intercom commentary. Nina texted me. She would be there at the station to meet me.

An hour outside of Seattle it was time to pull myself together. I went down the initially scary narrow stairs, now fun, and there, in the vestibule, were two Park Service volunteers, standing with their portable intercom machine. Here was source of the commentary. They were nice retired men in Park Service uniforms, and someone had complained of their previous presence in the Observation Car and the vestibule was where they ended up. "Of all things!" I said to them, my new buddies. It's not like they were non-stop talking in obnoxious voices. It was pithy information delivered in pleasant tones with plenty of long silent spaces. I think most Americans love the Park Service. I know I do. I talked to them during a few of their interludes and it was interesting to watch them when they were working. They took turns speaking. They had a script. They knew their stuff and were smooth. They believed in what they were doing.

I thanked them and went into the hall of bathrooms and chose the one at the end, the one with the counter room, where I brushed my teeth, washed my face, re-did the braid, and changed into my clean shirt. The Arizona woman from breakfast came in. There were two sinks, plenty of room for two. I was glad to see her again. During breakfast she had said something about her Dad and World War II, and I wanted to know more. Her father wanted to go to war, but was asked by the government to stay on his ranch and raise beef for the soldiers. That's what he did, but it was hard for him, she said. Of course it was.

Back upstairs, I packed up my pillow and blanket, my knitting, my souvenir cup. I kept *The Warrior's Honor* out and read some and looked at the new scenery of water and the outskirts of Seattle. The intercom commentary changed accordingly. We were riding down the side of Puget Sound. Seattle, I learned, had the largest ferry system in the country.

When a passenger plane has taxied into place at the end of a flight, some people get right up and stand in the aisle and wait there, while others sit and wait. It's the same when a train pulls into the station at the end of the line. Birdie was up before we stopped. She was among the first. My diagonal, the conversationalist, kept his seat. I kept mine and so did Rock. We all waited a while. I guess they were letting the first floor people off. My diagonal was talking to his seatmate, and it was a pleasant distraction to hear the voices. No one else was talking. I think this very last wait was especially hard for Birdie. She looked toward my diagonal, leaning to see around the people in between. "I've never heard anyone who talks as much as you!" she let out. I winced.

The line began to move. We seated people got up. "Goodbye, Gabby!" called out Rock to my diagonal, laughing. Goodbye. Goodbye.

Adelina, the kindhearted attendant, was on the platform, telling us all goodbye. "Don't forget about me!" she said to me.

"I won't!" I said.

There we all were, going toward the station together, with all our things.

It seemed strange. I'd gotten used to my life on the train with these people. Inside the station, it was dark after walking in the sun. Strange again, and, as I was looking around and adjusting to the relative darkness and noticing the high-backed wooden benches, I saw Nina. Surprise! An old friend. It felt surprising to see an old friend after days of traveling by myself.

"You look good!" she exclaimed. "I thought you'd be tired and dragging!"

I smiled. Nina always looks good. We went to lunch, then she dropped me at her house and went back to work. I unpacked, and found in my pants pocket, floating free, the one-hundred dollar bill I had carefully sewn into the bottom. This set off a momentary, irrational wave of panic. Is this some kind of a joke? I thought.

Showered, in clean clothes from the suitcase, full of celebratory energy, I went on a walk to explore the neighborhood. It was a beautiful day.

I liked Seattle. I hadn't expected that. I knew I'd enjoy my time with Nina and her husband, and my time alone when they were at work, but I had not expected to like the city, in and of itself. A city's a city, I had thought, and I'm no longer interested in cities. But I loved the spirit that Seattle's neighborhoods have. There was even a homemade museum of its different neighborhoods that I found on one of my walks. I loved the lavender everywhere, the highly individual and exuberant gardens spilling out onto the sidewalks, the way people stopped their cars in both directions when I waited on the sidewalk to cross, even on busy streets. I loved all the water, and watching boats go by, all kinds of boats.

We took a ferry to the Olympic Peninsula and camped for two nights on a wide beach beside the Pacific Ocean. That's the kind of thing you do when you have an adventuresome friend like Nina. We had driftwood logs for our camp seats, and explored beach and bays and tide pools during the day. At night we could see other distant campfires along the beach, but, day and night, it was more like having the place to ourselves.

CHAPTER 22

Taking The Long Way

Driving back to the train station on the last morning in Seattle, Nina questioned me, laughing, about my train plans home. "Are you *sure* you want to do this?"

"Oh, yes, I'm sure," I said, lying. At a red light she picked up her new Smart Phone and found the next flight to Charlotte, before the light even changed.

"I could take you right to the airport," she said. "You could be home tonight."

"Thanks," I said, throwing in a laugh of my own. "I'm good for the train."

It was excruciating, having her pull up the airline information, and so quickly at that. Knowing now what the train was like, and having discovered that it was mostly good, and even great at times, didn't seem to make much of a difference. An insistent part of me was saying, OK, you've done it once, now let's just get home. That's what I wanted to do, get home as quickly as possible. Slowing down is not hard, but it is very different. So different. Nevertheless, happy or not, I was going to take the train.

There was a traffic snarl around the entrance to the station and Nina had to go to work, so when we were a half-block away I told her to let me off. "I don't mind getting you closer," she said.

"No, no, this is great, this is good," I said, and I thanked her for everything and got my suitcase and daypack out of the back and came around to her window and said "Thank you" again, and "Goodbye," and I waved, and set off for the station, and loneliness came crashing in to replace entirely the feelings of dread.

How could a young, energetic city like Seattle have a train station so dismal? I said to myself.

The outside might have been fine. I don't remember anything about it. I wasn't paying attention. I was self-absorbed. But the inside was dark.

It wasn't really that dark. In the seconds it took for my eyes to adjust it was fine. There was plenty of light. It was just that I was in such a bad mood.

I couldn't tell where to go. Inside was one big room and filling the room were what looked like three long lines of people. The lines curved and were close enough that maybe there were only two instead of three. I couldn't tell where the lines were headed and could only guess where to join one. The ends weren't distinct. They were like ropes that had unraveled. Nobody seemed worried or upset. I asked a casual group of people who may have been the unraveled end of one line if they were in line, and they said yes, and that they were in line for the train going to Portland. That wasn't me. I was going back to Chicago.

I asked at the end of another line, and these people were going onto the *Empire Builder*, like me. They weren't sure this was the right line, but they thought so, and I stuck with them.

The line hardly moved. I looked around the station. At the top of the high walls of this large room were windows, and leaning out under the windows, almost horizontal, were box fans, presumably for air circulation. One could trust that they were securely attached, but one could also doubt. No one else looked at them.

You could see the motes of dust floating in the light from the high windows. The whole scene had the monochromatic brown look of an Ellis Island movie set. It could easily have been beautiful. I might have pretended that I was a new immigrant coming to America, on a big adventure of opportunity, but you can't do that kind of thing when you feel dispirited.

The talk from the people around me centered on the train coming in from Portland. It was late. The *Empire Builder* wasn't going to leave until the Portland train got in, and maybe not until it left again to go back to Portland. We weren't going to leave on time, news that only depressed me further.

I had decided to check my suitcase for the trip back East. I didn't care if anything happened to it. I'd spent some time rearranging, and in my train things, in the mesh backpack, I now had the bare essentials of toiletries. I'd put the Hawaiian print bathroom bag, which had taken up a lot of room and contained things I wouldn't need, in my suitcase. The neck pillow was in the suitcase as well, along with the headlamp, the washcloth, and a sleeping shirt I didn't use on the first trip. I'd thrown away the cheap eye shades, which felt too silly to be helpful. One strap had broken off anyway. I didn't bring any apples, and brought two trail mixes instead of four. I still had a lot of things, and my backpack was still a balloon.

Our line's destination was a makeshift counter sitting on its own away from the wall of the room, and working there was an agreeable and seemingly efficient woman about my age. I told her I wanted to check my bag all the way to Greenville, South Carolina. She'd never heard of that Greenville, and had to look it up to make sure it was a station that could receive checked bags. I apologized for the inconvenience. "Oh, no," she said, "don't apologize. It's a relief to do something different." And, yes, she said, finding Greenville in her book, you can check your bag all the way through, so she tagged my suitcase and, no, she couldn't say when we would be leaving.

I found an empty section on one of the high-backed wooden benches and sat down to wait, mournfully. There was once a time in my life when I decided that the word "endure" was wrong and that everyone should use "persevere" instead. Brother. If anyone had suggested that to me while I waited, I would have looked away.

It is almost shameful to write here about Aung San Suu Kyi, but I will leave mournful me enduring away on the high-backed wooden seat in the peaceful Seattle train station, and do it anyway.

Ms. Suu Kyi, you may know, is from Myanmar, which used to be called Burma. She lives there still, in 2019 as I write.

She has been known to talk publically about her faith in democracy, a dangerous thing to do if your country happens to be ruled by a group of military men unwilling to share power. In 2011, the year of my train trip, that was indeed the case. By then, she had spent a total of fifteen years under house arrest, separated from her husband and two sons.

During a time of house arrest in 2011, she recorded a speech that was smuggled out of Myanmar and broadcast by the BBC. In her speech she said that one way a person can live with fear is to "pretend to be unafraid." And if your friends are also in danger, you can pretend not to notice that they "are also pretending." Suu Kyi was frank about her bravery. She said she sometimes felt "laid low by anxiety and uncertainty." She found inspiration and courage in the stories of other freedom fighters.

A July 18, 2011 editorial in the *Christian Science Monitor*, my source for the story of the smuggled speech, added this: "When asked how it felt to be free after her most recent house arrest, she responded that she was no different 'because my mind had always been free.'"

I sat without happiness on the bench in the Seattle station for a long time. Then a woman my age walked up and sat near me. She wasn't right beside me but close enough that I could hear the phone conversation she started after she sat down. It was quickly obvious that she was talking about a wedding dress being chosen, and before long it was clear that the wedding was her daughter's. She was talking to a friend, maybe her husband, maybe someone else in the family. She was questioning herself on this dress business. Had she been as helpful as she could have been? Guilt was trying to snare her, and doing a pretty good job.

She ended her phone conversation, put her phone away, waited a moment, and leaned over and started a conversation with me. Was I waiting for the *Empire Builder*? I moved closer, and we waited together and talked about weddings and other things. When it was finally time to board, we were assigned to different cars because she was getting off somewhere in Montana, but once the train started she came forward and found me, and we sat together again. Her name was Susan. When someone came around taking dinner reservations, we made two for eight-thirty.

CHAPTER 23

Me And You

S usan and I were seated for dinner with two young people, a young woman and a young man. They were not traveling together. I ordered the salmon, which was thick and fresh and perfect, with a perfect pan-dripping sauce. The young woman was a college student, Latina, lovely and poised, and was traveling to visit family in St. Paul. The young man was a high-schooler, White. He had just finished up his summer job as a counselor at a camp outside Seattle and was going back to his home on the East Coast. That should have been impressive to me, his traveling across the country by train, since I was so scared and resistant doing the same thing as a supposedly mature fifty-nine-year-old, but such was not the case. I was totally impressed, and not favorably, by his table manners. Thank goodness for lovely Susan.

She led the conversation in her graceful, friendly way, and if she noticed his manners at all, she wasn't trapped by them. She was interested in the lives of these two. The boy's mother, we learned, had died a short while ago. The young woman responded to this with an easy grace of her own. "I know what it's like to live without one of your parents," she said, with simple kindness, and we went on to other things.

The world is filled with lovely women.

When I returned home, inspired by meeting the man who had lived in Ethiopia, I tried, then gave up on, finding the right book about that country. Then the right book appeared. It is about Ethiopia, but mostly about a lovely woman, Haregewoin Teferra, "ebullient and round," who took in orphans.

Ethiopia is upper-middle on the east side of Africa, almost reaching the coast, but not quite. Considered the birthplace of world-wide human migration, and also the coffee bean, it is where Paul Salopek started his journey following humanity's path. The book I found, *There Is No Me Without You*, published in 2006, was included in a magazine listing of books that readers said they enjoyed. I gave it a try, and it was the one. If Ethiopia is where humanity got going, then the story of this Ethiopian woman, and others around her, could lead one to believe that humanity is doing all right after all.

"On a dim, clattering afternoon in the rainy season, I sat in a crowded living room in Addis Ababa…"

So begins the book, and author Melissa Fay Greene is the "I" in that room. It was not a special day or a special meeting. The crowd in the living room were friends of the woman Haregewoin (Har-eg-eh-*woin*), just dropping by to see her. Some were retired, some unemployed. The economy was sluggish. Some were "loyal" friends, some just "curious." Rain was pouring down, "drumming the tin roofs" of the neighborhood, "deafening." Coffee was served. "The mud yard boiled and popped." The visitors came in, shook off their wet wraps, "squeezed in to join the inactivity," and sat, content. All but the one *ferange* (white), American author Greene. The squeezing and the inactivity were driving her crazy. "The hard rain pummeled the roof, stirred up the courtyard, and sent hordes of barefoot little kids galloping past Haregewoin's open door." Greene, a journalist, had come to Ethiopia to get to know Haregewoin and the children and their country. She sat impatiently, she endured, for "long hours," feeling "overwhelmed" by the "group inertia."

But eventually something did happen. The phone rang. It was someone from the county government, which called often, always with the same question. Can you come and get another child? Haregewoin paused with the phone at her ear, partially for effect, partially to calculate her resources. Yes, she then said, and she and Greene and Greene's driver drove to the part of the city where two-year-old Mintesinot, "delightful and confident," lived with his loving Dad on the sidewalk, both of them sleeping nights on a pile of rags enclosed by a low wall of scrap tin and wood, a sheet of plastic their roof when needed.

The boy Mintesinot was "the prince of the neighborhood," beloved by all. "Hush," said neighbors to each other as they walked by and saw the little boy asleep. "Baby is sleeping."

He sobbed to be taken away from his father who, with painful sadness himself, let his most precious son be taken. The father was dying of AIDS. The mother had already died. This was 2004.

The Communist coup of 1974 in Ethiopia, mentioned by the gentleman on the train in his telling of the "unsavory tale," evolved into the dictatorship of Colonel Mengistu, who was in turn toppled by Meles Zenawi in 1991. Both revolutions were extremely bloody. Four years later, Meles was elected prime minister, and hopes were high. But the problems were huge. Watching their leaders become "dictatorial and martial" was "a source of momentous disappointment and discontent" to those who had hoped for a bit more democracy.

Meanwhile, the AIDS epidemic was building. By 1999, millions of parents in Africa were HIV positive and dying, and there were millions of orphans. Ethiopia was overflowing with orphans. Haregewoin did not set out to take in orphans. In 1999, she was suffering from unrelenting grief. Her seemingly healthy husband had died from a heart attack nine years earlier, and then one of her two daughters, a quiet book-loving girl, married with a child of her own, died from a long and slow wasting disease which is not named for us. Haregewoin was bereft. She was a believer and tried devotion. She went to one church or another every day for a year, but found no relief. She considered herself "ruined," "useless." She finally decided to go into seclusion. She would move into a hut bordering a cemetery and live an unadorned life of prayer. She made a final round of churches to say good-bye, but the director of charity at her favorite Catholic church had already planned to ask her to take in an orphan.

"But you know I'm not Catholic."

This was met with a laugh. "That doesn't concern us!"

Haregewoin loved children. She thought maybe helping someone was better than seclusion. She thought maybe this was God's will. She agreed to take the child. One child soon became many. Word spread. There were so few people helping in the beginning. AIDS was a terrible disease, and also a considered a stigma. Haregewoin took in more children than she thought she could care for, but if you love children, how do you say no when a dying mother knocks on the gate and begs you to take her baby? You do say no, because you are tired and have too much responsibility and because there are never enough beds, food, or money, to say nothing of time and energy. But you know this dying mother is right when she says there is *no place else*, and you take the baby. You take him into the two-room house you can afford at the beginning, because you have left behind your job and your very middle-class life for the life of an unpaid caretaker of many.

Haregewoin experiences ups and downs, but keeps coming back to life when hit with sorrows or the consequences of her own mistakes. She comes back not at all because she is super-human, as Greene is careful to show us. Haregewoin comes back because she knows how to return. She knows how to love, especially children, but grown-ups also. When she feels depleted, when there are too many children and she doesn't have enough help, then she takes care "in a maternal style." What does that mean? "Your hands can stroke, your lips can smile and kiss, your voice can soothe, but your mind veers away." And Haregewoin had a commander side. That's the only kind of person who could have managed all those children. Her capacity for love gave her the kindness to do it well.

Ethiopia and coffee are intertwined, and we are present many times for the "coffee ceremony" at Haregewoin's house. The beans are roasted in an iron skillet, ground in a mortar and pestle, then brewed in a handmade urn. In a most poignant scene, Haregewoin serves to the Spanish woman who has arrived to adopt, to take away, the child that Haregewoin has come to love the most. Is she delaying? She politely insists that coffee be made. Is being hospitable so ingrained? Is it what she does when she is anxious?

I love this book. It restores me. I am grateful for the photographs, and for Greene's words that give pictures beyond the power of photographs. Here is the courtyard of Haregewoin's house when the rains have stopped:

> "As usual, it was busy. The minor-key notes of grief were being drowned out by the percussion of childhood: hopscotch, hand-clapping games, the *oof!* of a deflated soccer ball kicked into the air, wet clothes slapped across the laundry lines, and the slide and whack of a jump rope. A eucalyptus tree stirred in the hot wind beside the fence, its small dense leaves making a high-pitched rustling noise."

Yes, there are sad stories, but joy is abundant. Greene is careful not to be maudlin or sensational. This book is much more about life than death. Even dying can be tender, because of Haregewoin's home and because of how Greene chooses to see. Betti, four years old, HIV positive, is brought to Haregewoin's by her widowed father. He leaves her to stay, but visits every Sunday, wearing a coat and tie. He, too, is HIV positive. One Sunday he does not show, sends word that he is in the hospital, and doesn't come again for a month. When he returns, the tie is gone and he is moving much slower. He smiles and nods, "as if the slow motion were a form of gallantry." He and Betti grow sicker. They sit together on their Sundays, she "propped against her father's leg," and watch the other children playing in the courtyard, "the two of them still and peaceful in one another's company in the assembling twilight."

The final section of the book follows four American families who adopt older children from Haregewoin's home. Early in her life with orphans, Haregewoin learned that no one would adopt any child older than three. Then someone told her another story. "The Americans will adopt anyone." She found out about Merrily and Ted Ripley, of Port Angeles on the Olympic Peninsula of Washington State, who operated two orphanages for older children in Addis Ababa and helped with adoptions. Haregewoin rented a van, scrubbed twenty of her oldest, gave instructions. "Be smart!" "Use good manners!" "Use your English!" She drove them to meet "unflappable" Merrily, who was expecting to meet only Haregewoin, and a new partnership was formed.

Greene cautions readers many times to remember that out of country adoptions are only a tiny part of the solution, for many reasons. Ethical agencies, she says, always try to find homes in the child's country. Before AIDS, any orphan in Ethiopia was swept up by the extended family. Haregewoin herself worried that American children were not raised to be as well-mannered as she thought they should be. But the adoption chapters that finish the book are grand. Not sugarcoated; one of the four adoptions depicted is gruelingly challenging, and also grand.

Here in this section we see Mintesinot again, "Minty," the little boy who lived on the sidewalk with his father. Minty is still "delightful and confident." He plays in the pool at his new Colorado home and does crunches with his wrestling coach dad. He has on his dresser, and kisses, a photo of his first dad, holding his hand on the street of his first life.

I wondered, as I neared the end of the book, if Greene would be able to equal the terrific first chapter with the last. She does. We are in Ethiopia once more. Mikki and Ryan of Atlanta want to find the grandfather of the orphaned sister and brother they have traveled to adopt. The grandfather is the one who brought the children to Haregewoin's. Leaving the city to search for the grandfather's village "in a cold, gray downpour" are the new family of four, plus Greene, plus Selamneh, Greene's driver and translator, all packed into Selamneh's little taxi. They first find Haj, a local elder, the one who knows everyone, and after the graciously offered and obligatory refreshments served in his backyard, they pile again into the car, Haj in the passenger seat, the rest in the back, and they continue the search. On the side of the road they come unexpectedly upon Aunt Fasika, who joins in the back. They drive slowly beside an open-air market and Aunt Fasika looks for her father. A group of young men runs up to surround the car and pound on the hood, frightening the Americans, but word has spread and the young men have found grandfather. "Through the rain,

Addisu came painfully jogging." He watches quietly as each adult gets out of the car, then when his grandchildren emerge, he touches their faces, he cries, he picks them both up, one for each arm, he smiles with joy. He has not seen his grandchildren for a year, and certainly doubted whether he would ever be seeing them again.

He then asks if Mikki and Ryan want to see the graves of the children's parents, and everyone gets into the car again, with grandfather added to the back, "where people now lay like pieces of firewood atop one another." Selamneh manages to get the old car up the long road to the church and graveyard. Villagers follow the car, the priest comes out from the church, and a second, impromptu, funeral is held.

In the silence after the priest speaks, Mikki whispers to Ryan, "Say something."

"I'm not a great public speaker," he protests, in a whisper.

But he realizes he must, indeed, say something. Reluctant, big friendly White man Ryan makes his way self-consciously over to Selamneh, mumbles something into Selamneh's waiting ear, and the crowd murmurs. This was a great village event, but who precisely was this White man? Who was the African American woman who had been standing with him? Who was the White woman Greene? The African translator?

What follows in this speech, in this scene, is everything that means anything, the family of man, a Gettysburg address of the modern world, whispered first by Ryan, in pieces, then delivered, loudly and confidently, in translated pieces, by Selamneh, who "always had a heart for the poor," to the assembled villagers, many crying, family and friends of the living and the dead, in Amharic. The story in its full is an exquisite best-of-humanity tale, told exquisitely. "We are all one family now."

CHAPTER 24

Nice People In Montana

"Mon-TAN-N-N-N-a-a-a…"
That was the neighbor behind us, behind Susan and me.

"Mon-TAN-N-N-N-a-a-a…"
We couldn't see him. He talked goofy.

"Mon-TAN-N-N-N-a-a-a…"

This was only the latest offering. He talked a lot. He spoke in a moderate voice, easy to hear, but not so loud as to be annoying, to me. It was entertaining. I pictured him as a big White guy. This was the morning. We'd just gotten into Montana, or so I supposed.

"Mon-TAN-N-N-N-a-a-a…"

Susan and I did not mention our neighbor or his talk. We had our own things to talk about. She'd gone back to her seat after our dinner of the night before. A seatmate had joined her spot in the afternoon when she was up with me, and I felt bad about that because the empty seat she'd created by coming to visit me was obviously enticing to someone boarding. Seats were gradually filling as we traveled east, but I was by myself during the night.

We talked about the wedding dress again. "Don't beat yourself up," I said.

For the weekend ahead, a weekend for making wedding arrangements, her daughter was traveling home to Montana. There were appointments with photographers and florists, and visits to the church and to possible places for a rehearsal dinner. There was a lot. "You'll do fine," I said.

Susan took the train to Seattle often. Once she tried a sleeper, but she didn't like it. "I felt isolated," she said.

"I like these people, you know?" That was our goofy neighbor. Who was he talking to? He was talking about the Amish. There was an Amish family, mother and father and children, in our car. "Smiling, happy, the little things in life," he said. "They know how to do it."

Susan got off at her Montana station, telling me to look her up if I ever came back. She was one of the nicest people I've ever met. The goofy guy, whom I still hadn't seen, struck up a conversation with his across-the-aisle neighbor. The neighbor was a heavy young Black man. It turned out that he had a terrible stutter, so I was nervous for him. But they conversed, in spite of my nervousness, all talk led by the goofy guy. "Where are you going?" "What are you doing there?" "First time on the train?" This and more, followed by a hearty ending. "Nice talkin' to ya, man!" I loved them both, and loved America. When, an hour later, the goofy guy made the loudest possible noise slurping his drink with a straw, I made myself OK with that. He'll be a fast drinker, I told myself.

There was a train magazine in the pocket in front of me, and I read about the renovation going on in the Seattle station. So that was it. Renovation, not neglect. I should have figured.

Surprise! Goofy guy had a seatmate. I couldn't hear her at all, and only assumed she was a her. He talked about what I gathered was a planned trip to Japan.

"We'll ride the bullet train, and be going so fast we'll be scared out of our mind!

"We'll be sitting there eating sushi in some little town, in some mom and pop place.

"Let's go to Japan, before we di-i-i-i-e. Let's spend our money."

He asked questions of his seatmate.

"How many times have you seen Mt. Fuji?"

(Couldn't hear the answer)

"Where does your sister live? Doesn't she live near Tokyo?"

(Have they just met?)

"Today's Wednesday, isn't it?"

(Not an uncommon train question)

"Hey, they just called Taylor."

(For the Dining Car, for lunch)

"Is that you? Taylor?"

They got up to go to the Dining Car and passed me. He was a big guy, White, about forty. She was a little old Asian woman.

Five hours later, I heard him, back at his seat behind me, hail the attendant and order them both salmon for dinner, with rice. "Lice," he said. He ordered it brought to their seat. I didn't know you could do that.

Philip Glass: "I travel the world, and I'm happy to say that America is still the great melting pot…"

Not a perfect melting pot, he goes on to say, but a better one than anyplace else he'd been.

My goofy neighbor, a phenomenon strictly for our little neighborhood, our grouping of seats in the back of the car, was not the most outstanding personality in our car. That award went to Russell. He was a man-about-the-train type, curious and friendly. You'd see him everywhere. "Hey, Russell!" you might hear as he passed down the aisle. Everybody knew him, everybody liked him.

Russell was intrigued with the Amish family in our car, and I saw him in long conversations with the father and, separately, with the teenage son. I guess he was trying to figure out the Amish. Who wouldn't be curious? And I guess the curiosity went both ways. Russell was Black, and there weren't many Black people on our train. Back East, it was different. On the *Crescent*, half of the passengers were Black, maybe more than half. It was heartening on my travels to be in a Black and White America that got along fine, at least tolerating each other and sometimes getting to know each other.

"Mr. New York. That's what I call you. Just kidding."

That's what I overheard someone saying to someone. I think the speaker was talking to Russell, but I can't be sure because I didn't write that down. If the speaker was talking to Russell, I wonder why they thought of him as Mr. New York. Maybe he looked urban to them. Or because he had that quick humor. Or just because he talked fast.

"You know I was born in New York," the someone, I think Russell, answered.

"Really?"

"Yeah. But I get scared real easy."

"You're a Teddy Bear."

"Yeah, I'm a Teddy Bear."

I won an opportunity for redemption at dinner. I was seated with the high-school boy again, the one I'd disliked at first because of his table manners. I made good. The boy and I greeted each other warmly and started our conversation right off. We sat with a lawyer my age traveling by himself home from a family reunion in Seattle. He was afraid of flying. He was nice, but a little distant. Maybe worried. He said he'd brought work with him, a case involving a split in a church congregation and a subsequent battle over who owned the church building. He wasn't getting as much work done as he had wanted. Maybe that was the cause of his quiet.

I ordered my usual glass of wine, but they were out. The lawyer had a beer, but I didn't want beer, so I had a gin and tonic. That kicked me up a notch. The boy and I were friends, but there was the problem of the lawyer's apparent melancholy. He talked about his case a little and I talked about *The Warrior's Honor*. The boy said he hadn't brought a book but wished he had. "I've got a book for you," I said, and I told them about *Riding the Iron Rooster*.

Perhaps you remember: *Riding the Iron Rooster* is Paul Theroux's story of the year he spent traveling around China by train. I'd packed my paperback copy. I'd brought it because I had remembered that someone spit on the floor on one of Theroux's trains.

I had broken my self-imposed rule of "one book" because of that last item. If things turned out to be bad on my train trip, I told the lawyer and the boy, I could use up some of the miserable time by trying to find that part in the book. I thought probably nothing on an American train would seem so bad. The lawyer and the boy laughed. I mean no offense to the Chinese people! I added, with gin-hyped passion. People are people. And some Americans do things that gross me out, too, I said.

On my way back to my seat after dinner, the triumph of getting the laugh from the lawyer plus the buzz from the liquor afforded me an atypical athletic confidence. I tried the balancing trick suggested by one of the car attendants in a welcoming speech. You lightly touch the tall back of every other seat as you pass down the aisle when the train is moving. I tried it, and did it well. I was pleased with myself.

All this grandiosity left me singularly unprepared for the shock of seeing someone in my aisle seat, and not just any someone. A man with shaved head and big wild eyes, a tank top, tattoos down both arms, shorts, hairy legs and sandals. Not your standard train passenger. He smiled and said "Hi."

My shock gave way instantly to a big smile with an accompanying happy "Hello!" and I stepped confidently and perfectly over his hairy legs into my window seat.

I introduced myself with animation.

He was Mitch. He couldn't have been any nicer.

CHAPTER 25

A Good Beginning

M itch was traveling to visit a friend, and the two of them were going to the drag races, some big-time drag races. What do I know about drag racing? "You do wear ear protection, right?" He laughed. My question was meant to be funny but the concern was genuine. I like being able to hear well and I liked Mitch. He was friendly and sharp, funny, and we had just met. Nothing was in the way. He was easy to like. I was the older, by ten or fifteen years I guess. I never thought to ask. We were both Bruce Springsteen fans, we discovered early on, me the mostly Part I Springsteen fan, he the Part II current one.

Springsteen started out on FM when FM was a culture apart, playing whole rock albums by musicians like Bruce who weren't pop enough for AM. That was the early seventies. I wasn't listening to much of anything then, except AM in the car. It was after college, and I'd moved in with my parents. (Feel free to pity them. I was not always easy.) I had no friends left in my hometown and was looking for a job as a waitress. It was just on the border of an "ain't goin' nowhere" scene, a scene that might make one buy an album (*Born to Run*) just because it made the cover of *Newsweek*, to which I had a subscription, the kind of scene that might lead one to dance in the basement when the parents were out of the house. What dancing Bruce inspires!

I danced alone. Mitch went to concerts with friends, not quite as much fun as dancing alone in the basement, in my book, but a close second. He'd been to five so far. He asked me if I knew any Bruce jokes. I didn't.

"Bruce!! Bruce!!" Mitch pumped his fist in the air.

"That's the first hour," he said to me.

"Bruce!! Bruce!!" Fist pump. Second hour.

Third hour—less energetic "Bruce! Bruce!" Less energetic fist pump.

Fourth hour—a weak "Bruce!" Weak fist pump. Fist turned in front of the face to check the time.

We laughed. We laughed out of love, you know.

In 2016, Bruce came out with his autobiography. There and in interviews he talked about how he has dealt with depression, in part by being on stage. "You're immediately pulled out of the inside of your head," he said to Terry Gross on National Public Radio. He went to therapy. "Yeah, I tend to be not my own best company."

"People see you on stage and want to be you," Terry said.

"I want to be that guy myself," he said. "I had plenty of days where I'd go, 'Man, I wish I could be that guy.'"

Who hasn't dealt with depression? Few that I know.

I didn't buy any Bruce Part II music because I wasn't buying any music then, but I heard it because Dee was a Part II fan. *The Rising* helped me as much as anything else with the sadness of 9/11. "May your hope give us hope. May your love give us love," he sings about those who responded. I will always be grateful for those words.

The Rising was no aberration. It seems that Bruce has always felt a sense of responsibility toward his world, even from the beginning of his music. This is what he told Terry Gross: "Our initial audience was a lot of young guys who you played a bit of a big-brother role for, and were trying to sort out a lot of the same things, right?" Being like a brother, "it was something that I worked pretty hard on."

My seatmate Mitch was a hunter, which was fine with me. I'm nervous about guns, but some of my friends are hunters, the responsible kind of hunter. If I were an animal, I'd want to be a wild animal. Mitch and I had been talking about the West, the land, and he was describing the beauty of some place, hill country somewhere, Reservation land as it turned out, and he knew it because he'd been invited to hunt there with some Native American friends. Native Americans don't willy-nilly invite a non-Native guy to go along on a hunt. I knew that, and Mitch was not Native. So I asked more. Yeah, said Mitch, his group of friends had to assure some others from the tribe that he was OK.

How does a person make friends outside his own group of people? By being bold and curious, by being a person of action and a respectful person. Mitch and I did not talk about this.

We talked about trains. We talked about families. Mitch said something mild about our president, which led me to believe that we were not going to agree on politics much. I gave a meaningless small smile to what he said and looked away a second and that was it for politics.

After two hours of conversation we were at that point of friendship and trust where important things can make an appearance. It seemed natural for Mitch to tell me about the time he killed someone. I had, indeed, formed my complete opinion of him, and I was completely on his side before hearing anything of the story.

He'd been at his house, late in the evening, watching TV with his girlfriend. Someone he knew, a man, came in uninvited, demanding something. I can't remember what that something was. I don't even remember if Mitch told me. It wouldn't have mattered what it was. I was Mitch's friend. The man had a younger man with him. Mitch didn't know the young man. It wasn't a friendly scene. Mitch told them to leave. The young man came at Mitch and Mitch reacted and shot him. There was a stunned silence. The young man looked dead. He was dead. Mitch called the police. The police came, detectives came, the police took everyone in for questions, and the detectives searched the house. "They didn't find anything," Mitch said. He was proud of that. I was too. He was released.

"I looked pretty strange back then," he told me with a laugh. "I had this long, thin beard." He demonstrated, pulling his coiled hand down from his chin. He was living in a small town. "Everybody knew who I was." That made things worse. "I walked through the grocery store the day after it happened, and people looked afraid of me and moved away from me." He laughed again, then looked ahead and was quiet for a moment. "I've wished a hundred thousand times that I didn't do it."

He figured that he couldn't stay in that town and moved away to live with his grandparents. He stayed in their basement, numb, for a long time. A preacher lived next door, and gave a hand to help lift him out of his hell of guilt and depression. Another man offered him a job, a repairman and carpentry job. "I told him the story right off. I knew he'd hear about it."

Mitch was the kind of guy who you'd guess would be a good craftsman and a hard-working, dependable employee. Capable, not a bluffer. He was very grateful for the people who helped him. He told me this. He told me about some cabinets he'd made for his boss from wood that was about to be thrown out. He was proud of doing a good job. Then we talked some more about family.

I asked about his tattoos. None of them were pictures. They were symbols, and he lit up when I asked about them. He pulled his right elbow out so that he could look at the top of his arm, and he touched the top tattoo. "This was my first," he said. He'd gotten it when he was on vacation somewhere on the Gulf of Mexico. It was a grouping of language characters from an Asian language and it translated "Drugs are Power." He and some friends had ended up at a tattoo parlor after a night on the town and he decided to get one, and picked that. The tattoo man told him to come back the next day if he still wanted it, which he did. There was also a hunting slogan, a love of family symbol of some kind that I don't remember, a Christian trinity symbol, and some others.

By then it was getting late. That was enough talking. It was time for sleep. I got out my pillow and blanket, we tipped our seats back, and Mitch went quickly to sleep while I lay there and thought about things.

Time passed.

Drugs are power. Who could possibly think that?

Time passed.

Maybe I thought that, and didn't realize it.

Time passed.

I think I did.

Time passed.

I can't get to sleep.

Time passed.

I can't get to sleep.

Time passed.

I'm never going to get to sleep.

CHAPTER 26

And Goodbye

I wasn't going to get to sleep in my seat, so I decided to go to the Observation Car, lie down on a bench of seats and sleep there. This presented the immediate problem of stepping over Mitch and not waking him. Not waking him. That was the crucial thing. I had to step over him, step over his stretched out legs, while holding my bulky blanket and pillow. Ready. Go. Success.

But every bench in the Observation Car was taken. There was someone lying down on every one. I stared at this dimly lit scene in disbelief, knowing that I did not want to go back and also craving the chance to be horizontal. I couldn't think. I could only stare. Just then, a fellow insomniac sat up from his spot. "You can have my place," he said, in a quiet voice befitting a quiet room full of sleepers. "It's not working for me."

"Thank you!" I whispered, as loudly as I could whisper. He gathered his sleeping things and left, and I made my bed and lay down.

It didn't work for me, either. It felt so good to lie flat. I was warm with my blanket, the pillow was just right, the quiet train rumble was, or should have been, relaxing, but I was suddenly obsessed with my backpack, way back in my own car on the floor at my seat. My stuff. What if something happens to my stuff? It was crazy obsessive possessive thinking, tangling my mind with ridiculousness, sending adrenaline everywhere. I knew it was crazy. The night crept by. I never slept. When it started getting light, I went back to my seat.

"My snoring kept you awake," said an awake and friendly Mitch. No, I answered truthfully, grateful that I could be truthful, and I told him about the Observation Car, and how people go there to lie down at night.

We started talking again and wound up with his grandmother, the one who had taken him in when he was lost. He told me, for the first time, that she had died recently, and he told me about her dying. It wasn't an easy death. She had cancer, a slow and uncomfortable cancer, and he talked about that, just giving the story. Then he started to frown, clench up, breathe faster. Here came the troubled thoughts. "I don't understand why really good people have to suffer." Mitch had grown angry. He wasn't looking at me. "She was always good to me, she always loved me, she was good to everybody. Why did she have to be in so much pain?"

I didn't say anything for a while.

"I don't know either."

He went on. "People say you're not supposed to ask God anything, you're not supposed to question God, but I'd just like to ask him why my grandmother had to suffer."

And there it was, one of those moments, a question, the question, so much full in the air, and nothing else in the world present at all.

"You can ask God anything you want," I said.

Suffering is the big question. People have many answers. Who knows the right one. Most answers don't make any sense to me. I suppose they make sense to the people who say them. I don't know if what I said made any difference. I don't know if it was even heard. Maybe it made things worse, more confusing. Maybe he dismissed it. I don't think my answer was even an important part of this. I think the important parts are asking and allowing and love.

The heat of the moment passed, for whatever reason, and we were on the train again and talking about other things, and before too long I wanted to move around.

"I think I'm going to try to find something to eat," I told Mitch.

I was too restless for the Dining Car so I went back to the Observation Car and down the steps to the Snack Bar. A tiny snack bar is the worst place for a breakfast, to my way of thinking, but better than nothing. I broke my return-trip coffee ban and got a coffee and a packaged cinnamon roll, and went back up to the Observation Car. Nothing was enjoyable. I was sleep-deprived, jangled, not fully wanting the caffeine of the coffee or the sugar in the roll, and afraid of hidden trans fats in the cinnamon roll, being that my father died of arterio-sclerosis, even though the wrapper claimed that there were no trans fats within.

Social people had already started coming into the car. I glanced at them and listened half-heartedly. Nothing interested me. Even the scenery failed to interest. Finally something interesting happened. A young family came in, a family that looked more awkward than the other groups. The father was a slender, short-haired, glasses-wearing, intellectual-looking type. The mother was pretty in a natural, outdoorsy way, and reserved. The two young children were attractive and reserved, like their parents. I wondered about their story for a while, but I was certainly ten times more uncomfortable than they were, because I was starting to feel guilty, on top of all the other wired-up things my body was feeling. I was thinking that I was being rude to Mitch. Awkward as I knew this was going to be, I also knew that I had to invite Mitch to join me. I left my coffee and roll on the table and went back to the seat.

"Hey," I said, coming up to our seats, feeling stupid, "I'm eating some breakfast in the Observation Car. Do you want to join me?"

I honestly did not think he'd want to come, but he said OK, and he got up and followed and sat down at my table. He didn't want anything to eat. I took a sip of my coffee and missed my mouth and coffee spilled down my shirt.

Mitch grinned. "Got a hole in your lip?"

It was a good-natured, buddy-to-buddy line, awkwardly delivered to a new female friend. We were overflowing with awkwardness. How I appreciated that line. Easily embarrassed me. Sigh. Such a nice guy. I gave a grin back, and there we were.

And I thought, Oh, man! Not halfway through the trip home and you've done in one of your two shirts! That's not good!

And wouldn't you know it, Mitch and the intellectual-looking dad started up a conversation. The train had slowed down for a station and was passing through the town. We saw a Walmart-type store, and Mitch made a comment to the dad, who was sitting next to us looking out the window, that there were fewer cars in the parking lot than one might expect this time of day and this time of year, and the dad agreed. It was not anything I would have thought about. Then they were off onto the economics of the region, which were volatile because of the North Dakota shale deposits, apparently. Then on to the specifics of the man's profession, something about setting up big events, and the cycles that big events go through, and the causes of those cycles, and so on. I sat back and began to enjoy my coffee. An hour later we slowed to pull into another station and Mitch stood up. "Well, goodbye. This is my stop." That took me by surprise. We shook hands and I said goodbye, and that was it. It was so sudden.

In writing this, I wish him all the best. I'd bet money he's doing OK. When he comes to mind, the thought is always a happy one. Sometimes I catch sight of a small cloud and think of Mitch. I always smile.

CHAPTER 27

Kettles Of The Glaciated Fringe

G oing East, I didn't see the small lakes on the prairie that had surprised me on the way to Seattle, maybe because I was preoccupied or maybe because we passed them at night. I didn't forget them, though. One evening, years after the train trip, I was reading contentedly from the latest *Daedalus Books,* when I came to a sudden stop.

Beyond Walden, by Robert M. Thorson, was the story of America's "kettle lakes," a type of lake found sprinkled in a band stretching across the northern part of the United States from New England to Montana. Those mysterious lakes I saw at first light out the window in North Dakota–could they have been kettle lakes?

Maybe.

"Kettle lakes" might seem an odd topic for a whole book. Author Thorson, who spent his childhood summers on Minnesota's Union Lake, would probably smile at that thought. In his "Acknowledgments," he thanks his parents for the lake time they gave him as a child, and adds that they were perplexed over the topic of his first book, the fieldstone walls of New England, where he then lived and taught geology. Though proud of their son's accomplishment, "they didn't quite understand why anyone would write a book about old fence lines." *Beyond Walden,* subtitled *The Hidden History of America's Kettle Lakes and Ponds,* was Thorson's second book, written in gratitude to his parents and all the others "who cherish small lakes…and want to help preserve them."

Walden Pond is "America's most famous kettle." Fictional Lake Wobegon, Thorson tells us, is certainly a kettle as well.

In Chapter One, we learn that glaciers are the reason for kettle lakes. Glaciers, when they recede, leave behind icebergs. The stranded icebergs, when they melt, make lakes shaped like bowls, like kettles.

The Laurentide Ice Sheet, the official name of our North American glacier, the one that created our kettles, was born in far north Canada a hundred thousand years ago, and grew in fits and starts until reaching its peak eighty thousand years later. At that peak it was almost two thousand miles wide. The thick center portion was two miles high, high enough to bisect the jet stream and send Artic air to Arkansas.

The glacier left its mark both coming and going. It carved the Great Lakes as it advanced. It pushed up and then left behind ridges of sand and gravel that formed Long Island and Nantucket. It left boulders behind. It left icebergs which made the kettles, and it ripped up "scabs" of tundra to form "prairie potholes."

It incorporated so much of Earth's water that sea levels dropped. North Carolina, far south of the glacier, was a hundred miles wider at the peak of the glacial age. Today's barrier islands are leftovers of the old river deltas.

Kettle lakes of the West are common sites for finding fossils of the huge Ice Age mammals, like mastodons and woolly mammoths. The Native American Ojibwe depended on the wild rice which grew in water at the edge of these lakes. Beavers, their fur highly prized by Europeans suffering from cold winters brought on by the Little Ice Age which began in the 14th century, lived on the shores of kettles.

Thorson describes the great impact of the beaver. "Like a powerful magnet, the supple skins of this aquatic mammal drew courageous Europeans deep into the heart of North America." What came with the Europeans was the beaver trade. The business plan seemed to be get all you can as quickly as you can and disregard any consequences. Native Americans were paid for beaver pelts, and with the trade came the end of the ecologically balanced Native American life of subsistence and the beginning of dependence on the European economy. When the trade died, the main source of Native income was selling land.

During the writing of his book, Thorson, a professor at the University of Connecticut, happened to be teaching a course on Thoreau's *Walden*. His "preparation for the course and the interaction with other academics and with his students greatly deepened his appreciation for Thoreau." That appreciation shows. His writing about *Walden* and the Transcendental Movement is some of the clearest and loveliest I've come across. Remember learning about the Transcendental Movement in high school? Dreadfully dull, I thought. Its inception was far from dull.

The quiet New England minister Ralph Waldo Emerson, at twenty-eight, was shocked by the death of his young wife, and forced to look outside Puritan thought for comfort. "Nature," he eventually declared, as Thorson paraphrases here, "was, or should be, an integral part of spirituality and religion." This idea, sustained and strengthened by Emerson's walks in the woods he owned by Walden Pond, began a cultural turn away from the strict, judgmental, icy aspect of 19th century Puritanism.

Then Thoreau took this inspiration another step. As Thorson puts it, Thoreau "fell in love" with Walden Pond. I believe it. Thorson gives a long list of writers who are in debt to *Walden,* and pays special tribute to Rachel Carson, whose *Silent Spring* awakened in

America an understanding of the crucial importance of ecology. She kept a copy of *Walden* by her bed.

Why did the glacier come and go? For a lot of reasons, but primarily because the shape of our orbit changes, over many, many thousands of years, moving from a more rounded ellipse to a stretched out ellipse, then back again. The different orbit shapes make for different weather.

That old glacier has almost completely melted, but not quite. There is a tiny bit left in the far North, under the ice cap on Canada's Baffin Island.

Were the mysterious lakes I saw from the train kettles? I don't think so. I'm guessing, from what Thorson says, that they were potholes. Potholes were also created by the glacier, not by leaving icebergs behind, but by picking up bits of tundra. Kettles and potholes can be hard to distinguish, apparently, but Thorson tells us that North Dakota "is the heart of the prairie pothole region, where isolated marshes, ponds, and small lakes are gems on the otherwise vast rolling prairie..."

CHAPTER 28

Ah, Chicago

The *Empire Builder* was going to be late getting to Chicago. We'd left Seattle hours behind schedule. We'd had to slow down for water again, and again at times we stopped for freight trains. "I hear it coming!" called out Mr. Mon-TAN-a, from the back of me, when an attendant explained a slowdown for freight. (He couldn't have heard it.) "Get out of the way!"

I wasn't upset about being behind schedule. I assumed they'd hold the *Capitol Limited* for us. After all, they held the great *Empire Builder* for the arrival of the Portland train. Right? Right.

But wrong. I was comparing apples and oranges, to say nothing of thinking wishfully. That all changed in an instant. We were told mid-afternoon, via intercom, that we weren't going to make our Chicago connections. "We'll be putting you up in a hotel," the announcer said. Don't worry, he implied.

I worried. I freaked, inwardly. I let rip with my choicest expletives, inwardly. I just wanted to go home. Enough of this! I've proved my point! I'm going to get a Greyhound and get home!

I was angry and afraid, but, like the vast majority of my fellow riders, I was quiet and appeared calm. I imagine most of us were upset, a least a little. I heard a few low grumblings, enough to make me think that the unease was general. I'm willing to call this a fairly positive picture of humanity. Maybe more than is recognized we humans can bend with the wind. I'd like to think that. A few of us, as I said, were vocal, but in a mild declarative and tension-relieving way, not a confrontational way. I remember Russell, good-natured, man-about-the-train Russell. He wanted to get home, too, and said so, in a grumbling voice. He was going to get a Greyhound, he grumbled. Even Russell, I thought.

Amtrak knew a thing or two about psychology. When they told us about the missed connections and the hotel rooms, they also told us they were going to have us all to the Dining Car for a complementary meal.

The meal was chicken fricassee. Warm, creamy, noodley and tasty. I sat with a woman going to the Mayo Clinic. She had to go often. Sometimes she couldn't drive afterwards, she told me, and she never knew beforehand whether she'd be able to drive or not, so she always took the train. We had been talking about plans and interruptions. I told her what train-pro friend Allison said. "You have to be flexible to ride the train." She liked that. She agreed.

"It helps in everything, doesn't it?"

Anna Raglan

"Yes," I said. It calmed me to discuss calming advice. We rode along.

6:40 p.m. was the time the *Capitol Limited* was scheduled to depart Chicago.

6:40 p.m. came and went. That was depressing.

We were told that someone would be boarding the train to help us with hotel reservations. When that someone did board, we were called in groups to the Dining Car. I made sure to move quickly when my group was called. An older woman traveling alone deserves the head of the line, I told myself. But, really, I was just scared, afraid of the unknown again. And impatient, again. I wanted to get moving, however I could. The official Amtrak helper was a man with owly glasses and an unhurried demeanor. He sat by himself in the first booth with a stack of papers, looking through his papers, not at us, as we entered. I sat in the booth next to him and the car gradually filled.

Before we could start on business, our attention was drawn to an altercation in the middle of the car. An older man and his wife were in one booth, and the man was talking with increasing loudness to an Amtrak employee sitting in the booth across the aisle from them. The man was complaining angrily about his missed connection, about missing a family birthday celebration. He went on and on. The Amtrak employee listened and responded respectfully, attentively. "Yes, I am sorry about the party you are missing." The man only got angrier and kept up his complaints. The rest of us watched.

Gradually, another thread to the story emerged, one that helped explain the level of the man's anger. On this trip, but on a previous train, he'd been in his sleeper car and was packing his suitcase getting ready to get off the train. The train pulled into the station and all of a sudden an attendant came to the door, excited, insisting, "You've got to hurry! Get your things together now! You've got to get off now!"

"I barely had time to get my shoes on!" he said, enunciating, red-faced, looking squarely at the Amtrak employee. "We got the bum's rush," he growled.

"I'm sorry," repeated our Amtrak man. Well-trained, I thought. By life and by Amtrak, I assumed. And what of the angry man's story? Maybe the sleeper attendant had made a mistake and hadn't given clear instructions at the proper time. Who knows? Maybe it was the man's fault. Maybe he hadn't paid attention. Regardless, I felt for him, I who know how enticing and blinding anger can be. But he was carrying this too far.

The Amtrak man, who happened to be young, finally drew a line. "Sir, I am sorry for your problems. But there is nothing we can do to make your connection. If this goes on much longer I am going to have to put you off the train at the next stop." This silenced the complainer, but he looked ready to explode. No one moved. All eyes in the car were on this scene. Then another young man, a passenger, sitting in the booth in front of the couple, spoke up. He was the youngest passenger in the car, early thirties, and as such he stood out. He was already turned towards the angry man.

"Look" he said, leaning just a little over the back of his booth. "It's too bad what happened to you. But we're all missing connections, and you just need to let these people do their jobs."

No one else said a word. He sure spoke for me, and I'd bet for all of us. There are times to bend with the wind, and times to speak up. He turned back around, his eyes met mine, and I gave a little nod of agreement. The angry man's wife put her hand on her husband's. "Let's go." Her face was unreadable. Had the train trip been her idea? They left the car. I hope they laugh about it now.

The one-on-one conferences with the hotel man began. I was one of the first. I can believe he was chosen for his particular job because of his patience. Me? I tried. But fear can be seductive.

A taxi? He'd just handed me twenty-two dollars (very considerate!) for taxi fare to and from the hotel. A taxi at night in Chicago?

"What if twenty-two dollars is not enough?" It was all I could think of to say that sounded reasonable and calm, when what I was thinking was anything but calm: Oh, God! Oh, my God! A taxi at night in Chicago!

He told me, calmly, without blinking an eye, that I could double up with some others. He said we'd be given hotel vouchers at the Chicago station. I let it go and thanked him and headed back to my seat. "Ladies and gentlemen," came a voice over the intercom, "I want to remind you that this is a non-smoking train."

I passed a second confrontation in progress, another between an attendant and a passenger.

"You go right ahead and report whatever you want," said the attendant, a woman, standing in the aisle, clearly angry.

"If I remember," said the passenger, a man outwardly more in control, but with a mean face. "By the time I get off this train I may have lost my memory."

"You just make sure you take good notes."

"Maybe I will."

"I've had enough of you, dude."

I also saw sweetness. I saw Russell sitting with the Amish father, lending his cell phone, showing how it worked.

In the Chicago train station we lined up at an Amtrak counter to get our hotel vouchers. I was near the head of the line, by design once again, and as I waited I surveyed, discreetly, those behind me. I got my voucher and waited at a short distance, and when the kind-looking older couple that I'd picked out got their voucher and turned from the counter, I approached them and asked if we could share a taxi. Yes, they said. Someone else had already asked, so there were four of us. The other person was a younger woman. She sat in the front seat of the taxi and I sat in the back with the older couple. We rode cozily through the city streets at night, always fun if you feel safe, and I wondered why on earth the young woman in front wasn't talking to the cab driver. Here we were in such an exciting big city with a driver clearly from another part of the world, and the young woman never said a word to him.

The hotel was brand new and the room comfortable. I cleaned up, went to bed happy, and made up for the sleepless night before.

The next morning we gathered in the lobby as we had arranged, and the hotel clerk called another taxi for us. The young woman of the night before wasn't there and another man had joined us. While we waited, we chatted, and the talk went to train travel. The woman of the couple repeated what I'd heard once before, that freight owns the tracks and gets the right-of-way over passenger trains. I said I was going to start a newsletter (baloney) about passenger train travel in the US. I was going to call it "All Aboard!" Then I said that I was riding because of climate change. I was trying to be frugal with my energy use. I told my bit about jumping off the ground needing more energy than staying down. The man who had joined us said that metal wheels on metal tracks use less energy than the rubber wheels of a car on a road, because there is less friction. That makes sense. I'd never thought about it.

Our new cab driver was Nigerian. He missed Nigeria, yes, but not too much. He liked Chicago. He didn't miss Nigerian food too much. I didn't ask specifically, but I guessed that meant he didn't even miss his mother's food too much. Chicago has good food, he told me. He liked Chicago food. I asked what his favorites were. He liked the pizza and the Chicago dog.

I had made a point to get a map of the city from the front desk of our hotel, and found on it a straight, that is to say uncomplicated, walk from Union Station to Lake Michigan. I asked at the station if this was a safe walk and they said it was. It was a great city walk. Midway, I noticed some strange planes in the air, ultra-fast little black jets. Then there were bigger jets drawing sky pictures. It was the Blue Angels. We'd seen the show in Seattle, and here they must have been practicing because there were no crowds. Few people were even looking. I sat in a little park and watched. My walk ended at the lake, where a white sandy beach completed the perfection.

A distance away, along the beach, I saw what might be a food stand. It was, and I was hoping they served Chicago pizza but they didn't, so I got another hot dog, just like the one I had going West. I sat in the sand to eat it while looking out over the lake. When I got back home to North Carolina, I found a larger map to check out Lake Michigan, and I believe it's the largest lake I've ever seen.

Walking back to the train station, I noticed a bookstore and gave myself permission to go in and find something, even though I hadn't finished *Warrior's Honor*. I was treating myself. I decided to try fiction, and I picked *Runaway* by Alice Munro. I'd heard good things about her.

At the station, Union Station again, more than an hour remained before our departure, and I did my best to find a place that sold Chicago pizza. "Why don't you sell Chicago pizza?" I asked the host at a nice-looking bar that served bar food.

"It takes too long to make," he said, with sincerity and regret, wanting me to appreciate the uniqueness of his city's dish.

CHAPTER 29

Leave The Driving

We who were to ride the *Capitol Limited* found out that we were going to take buses as far as Toledo. The seats on the bus were comfortable. Not quite as roomy as the ones on the train, but almost, and there were plenty, so single riders could have their own. I curled up and appreciated being in a novel setting, the bus.

There was political talk three rows ahead that I longed to join. I agreed with everything they were saying and they were three people, so were talking across the aisle, meaning it was easy to hear them. I did speak up an affirmation once, which was intoxicating, but I quit. They were far enough away that my joining in would have made me annoying. I could have moved, but they had enough people of their own.

They soon switched subjects, from politics to passenger trains, and brought up, no surprise, the pace of things.

"Don't be in a hurry. Don't be in any hurry."

"Yes. It only shortens your life anyway."

One of them had traveled out of the country. "Amtrak has been the one carrier I've been on that seems to care about its passengers." This comment brought politics back. "Every other developed country in the world subsidizes its rail service. People get upset about subsidizing the trains, but the airlines are subsidized like crazy." Then came the common assessment of who controls the tracks. "The freight calls the shots."

I don't know if any of what I heard is or was true.

Behind me was a softer story. Two men, in their early forties I guessed, were traveling with a few boys, maybe Scouts. The men were talking to each other about employment. One had just started a small business guiding people through health insurance. He was enthusiastic but nervous about the new venture. He sounded kind and careful.

"Forty years in corporate life," a man's voice came from the seat in front of me, "and I've heard it again and again. 'I have the magic bullet. I have the answer that will clean up all this mess.'"

I suddenly felt hungry and got out the last of my trail mix. Should I save some? I decided no, and ate it all. Should I take a nap, since I had two seats? I decided no. There's plenty of time, I thought. Six hours on the bus, we'd been told.

And now I was glad not to be part of any conversation. The countryside, Ohio I guessed, was pretty, and I wanted to read. Reading on a train or bus means read a little, watch out the window a little, and so on. What a pleasure.

Alice Munro, who writes short stories, I found surprisingly enjoyable. I think I had expected critically acclaimed modern short stories to be stilted, or arrogantly minimalist, or too teasingly mysterious. Somewhat of a chore, in other words. I had bought her collection called *Runaway,* and started with the first story, "Runaway." Very interesting. Beautifully interesting. There were surprises in the words she chose. There were surprises in the events, too, carefully presented in order to preserve the flow of the telling. It was a great bus ride. I remember the day getting slowly dark.

We changed back to the train in Toledo sometime during the night. A small group of employees were lined up on two sides to form a loose passageway for us as we walked through the station. They were joking with each other, and they smiled at us and greeted us. I've had a fondness for Toledo ever since.

The new train was another double decker. We had seat assignments and mine was on top, right at the top of the stairs. My seatmate was already there in his window seat, and we were just getting acquainted when I heard huffing and puffing and groaning coming up the steep stairs. The groaning gradually appeared and, oh my Lord, it was a man with portable oxygen. "Sit down!" I said, scrambling up, pointing at my seat. "Sit down and rest!" He took up my offer with a happy grin and a huffy thanks. I had to admire that grin. I'd like to say that my seat offer was purely charity, but it wasn't. If he'd collapsed, we'd have been delayed for hours. I started down the aisle in the stream of people getting on, looking for someplace to wait, when someone in one of the seats spoke. "You can sit here." It was a woman, in a window seat. It turned out to be Russell's wife! Who would have thought the man-about-the-train was traveling with anyone? This was Teresa.

These train trips were her idea. They'd been on many. Their friends couldn't believe they traveled this way. We laughed. She and Russell took the subway, she told me, when they went to visit New York, which shocked the friends even more, New York City subways being considered by a significant segment of the world's population to be as dangerous as it gets. We laughed again. She had her hair in curlers, which I loved. Where was Russell? I didn't ask. Off making friends, probably. Teresa was the quiet center of that marriage. I was glad to meet her.

The man with the oxygen passed by and thanked me with more good cheer. I was glad, and not selfishly this time, that I had given him my seat. I thanked Teresa in turn, went back to my place, and got to know my new seatmate, a young man in music school studying composition. We talked awhile. He seemed unsure of himself with respect to composing, not necessarily a problem. We rode and slept. At first light I went to breakfast, and when I came back he was composing. He had a laptop and ear buds. He nodded his head, waved his hands like a conductor, then stopped to type, and worked for two hours.

Somewhere along the way we stopped and got on buses again. We ended our travels riding through Washington, through streets of beautiful buildings, seeing sights we would have missed on the train. Getting off the bus, on a sunny, not-yet-hot morning, I saw my suitcase on a luggage cart. Hi, friend!

Two Amtrak ladies were there to receive us, and I told them how much I liked Amtrak. They laughed.

I walked around inside the stately Union Station and stopped to look at what people had for sale on tables they'd set up. I bought a scarf, then sat on a bench and finished my second Alice Munro story.

Alice Munro turned out to be not right for me, or so I thought at the time. Her writing was beautiful, and it was the greatest pleasure to let go and be carried along by her talent. That's how I felt while I was reading on the bus. But I didn't like that first story's ending. The ending was going along just fine until Munro carefully lay down a little something that stopped me short, as intended. That little something said there was big and scary trouble ahead, and the story ended. I don't require a happy ending. There are happy endings that are too sweet for me, and I can take a sad ending. I just don't like ominous darkness ahead as an ending, and a masterful whiff of darkness is the most chillingly potent. I require some hope.

I wasn't going to decide after only one story, so I picked another, the last in the book, and finished it sitting on one of the wide platform benches in the Great Hall. This story started out even better than the first. It is a thrill to find a great writer. But the ending was another hopeless one, or so I thought. This is for someone else, I thought. Just before time to go to the waiting area for the *Crescent*, I threw her book away. I didn't want to carry it.

Impetuous? Sassy? Frightened? Smart? I'm tough on fiction. Maybe fiction, and the choosing of it, is part of how we grow into our own story. Later on, I bought the book again and changed my mind about it, somewhat.

In the waiting area for the *Crescent* were, surprise, Teresa and Russell. I had never asked where they lived. Their grown daughter was there, too. Maybe she lived near DC and was traveling with them to visit home. I didn't ask. We made our introductions, then settled down to wait for the train. We were all ready to take it easy.

CHAPTER 30

Aside: A Winter Trip

I had one last train to catch—the *Crescent* again, going home. I assumed, mightily, and with enormous pleasure, that the venture to Seattle would be my one and only train trip. Even when it turned out to be good, my journey did not whet any appetite for travel.

What do you do, though, when your good friend Francie, the one who helped you get your Seattle tickets, up and moves to Rhode Island, and wants you to visit? I love Francie. Thus, February of 2013 found me holding up to the light an old, grey, thin, drapey, unlined, wool wrap-around coat, locating little moth holes for repair. That coat would be both coat and blanket, an exciting idea. It had a hood. I could play the mysterious woman walking the platform in the middle of winter, in Eastern Europe, during the war.

I drove myself to Greenville. Dee was away. The sun set before I'd gone far because it was winter. The road to Greenville, the right one this time, was unfamiliar and dark and nearly deserted.

I wasn't terribly excited about the book I was bringing, *Mrs. Lincoln and Mrs. Keckly,* by historian Jennifer Fleischner. I rarely read history, afraid I'll be bored. And the history of two women from the 1800s? They were so constrained back then, weren't they?

Well.

The mind can always be free, people are people regardless of the circumstances, and what people do in response to constraints can be surprising. These things I discovered anew, and these two women were not quite as controlled as I had imagined. They weren't the type, for one.

Fleischner tells good stories, and she does so as a responsible historian, with accuracy as the priority. These are stories you can lean on, set in a vivid and trustworthy evocation of past times. It was a great book. I should have known. My good friend Olivia, the last friend with whom I exchange Christmas presents, had given it to me for the Christmas we'd just passed. Over the forty years Olivia and I have known each other, she has led me well into the country of American history, and into the land of the Lincoln family especially. Olivia's an incomparable storyteller herself. She can spot a good tale, and she knows me.

Mrs. Lincoln is obviously Mary Lincoln and Mrs. Keckly is Elizabeth Keckly, called Lizzy, who was Mary's dressmaker in the White House. Lizzy was born enslaved and purchased her own freedom using her artistic talent as well as her prodigious sewing skills, and equally prodigious faith, drive, and intelligence. By 1861, she was living as a free Black woman in Washington, DC, creating beautiful and intricate gowns for the most particular of the particular society women of that competitive political town. Her fashion advice alone was highly prized. Mary Lincoln interviewed Lizzy on the day after the Inauguration, and as soon as Mary heard that Lizzy had sewn for society queen Varina Davis, Mary chose her over the three other applicants. Varina Davis, wife of the former Mississippi Senator Jefferson Davis, who was by then president of the Confederacy, had already left the city with her husband and children to return to Mississippi.

War broke out soon after the Inauguration, but even during the war there were formal occasions, and Mary wanted or needed new dresses. Each dress required planning and numerous fittings. The two women spent a lot of time together. Lizzy, a model of stability and tact, in contrast to Mary, became a part of the Lincoln family. She helped with the children, she combed the president's hair, and she became one of Mary's few Washington friends. She was also active in her free Black middle-class world, a hardworking and church-centered group intent on securing the blessings of freedom. She helped establish an aid society for the Black refugees pouring into the city, and inspired Mary to ask her husband for money to buy desperately needed blankets for people who had next to nothing.

Four years of war and the death of her son Willie strained Mary to the point of breaking, and then her husband was assassinated. Lizzy was one of the few people Mary could bear to see in her grief. It took Mary six weeks to leave the White House. New president Andrew Johnson lived and worked elsewhere until she moved.

It was hard for Mary to decide where to go and, finally choosing Chicago, she left with "scarcely a friend to tell her good-bye," as Lizzy later wrote. The train trip took fifty-four hours. Mary had begged Lizzy to accompany her and Lizzy at first refused, because of the needs of her business and probably the emotional toll, but she relented and traveled with Mary, staying with her for several weeks in Chicago. She was a skillful and sympathetic caregiver and a good friend. Both women, Fleischner points out, were intelligent and had grown up in mixed-race homes. "I consider you my best living friend," Mary wrote to Lizzy later.

Mary Lincoln's reputation, then as now, is mixed. She could be difficult, "a hellcat" she was called by one of her contemporaries, but she also had her supporters, "for she never hurt a flea and her bark was worse than her bite." That is how a White House employee remembered her. I like Mary and think that Lincoln would not have been president without her faith in him and her ambition to live in the White House. Certainly she helped him with his depression. I think she played her part, unknowingly mostly, in the walk toward legal and cultural equality.

Is Elizabeth Keckly a person who becomes familiar to American schoolchildren? I suspect so, these days. She should be. She was strong and courageous in circumstances few of us could imagine, and schoolchildren need to hear at least a little about some of those circumstances. She was generous, yet did not suffer fools. She was a successful and respected businesswoman. She valued both her self-reliance and her community. She absolutely played her part in the creation of a more perfect union. And, when no one else would or could, she cared for the widow of our assassinated president, a role which deserves American recognition.

In the winter of 2013, we on the *Crescent* rode northward at leisure, through North Carolina then Virginia, toward Rhode Island. I read of those in the White House who had lived at the center of our great national cataclysm. I read, or knitted, or snacked, listened to conversations, looked out the window at the snow. A snowstorm had covered the East Coast a few days before I was to leave. All the better. Tracks had to be cleared, but by the time I left, all trains were moving normally. There were beautiful snow scenes out the window all the way up.

I went to the Dining Car in the morning and had breakfast. I'd slept alright, but was feeling weird and wired. I wasn't even hungry, but I made myself get up and go, to move, to be social. I ordered the Regional Special, which was crab cakes. Someone had prepared these with care, without unnecessary ingredients, and with a light sauce that did not overwhelm the sweet crabmeat. They were as good as my mother's.

I sat with a man my age who grew up in the country in Louisiana. His mother could out-fish anyone around. He threw that out in passing, not thinking that it would mean much to me. It did. I loved it. Some men didn't even want to fish with her, he added.

If I could be anyone for ten minutes, I think I'd pick to be her, while she was fishing of course. I'd want to experience how it feels to know through and through about how fish are fish, what they choose to do. And I'd like to see her fishing country.

In my car, the best conversation came from two rows up. A group of four made friends across the aisle and talked about celebrities, who was or wasn't "going crazy," and about politics and food. The four were all from New York City, were headed home, returning from visits to family down South, and knew some people in common. Though we were winter travelers, one described summertime feasts spread out by her Southern kin outside under the oak trees. Homemade fried chicken and potato salad, fresh corn and tomatoes and green beans, peaches, homemade cake and pie. The others knew just what she was talking about.

The four talked with our attendant, who would stop for a moment sometimes when she passed through. The quality of the food on the train, I overheard the attendant say, in response to a question, depended on who was cooking.

"You must meet some nice people," said one of the riders.

"And you meet the mean people, too," she said. Like the ones who endlessly protest having to share a seat. "This is public transportation," she'd tell them. "Sometimes you have to share a seat." Some people would even buy two tickets so they didn't have to share. "Not many," she said.

For this trip I stayed on the train in Washington, and rode all the way to Penn Station in New York City, the northern end of the line for the *Crescent*. I bought lunch in the station and ate in the Amtrak waiting room, then took a commuter train to Rhode Island, "Little Rhody." Little Rhody is a water state. Staring out the window, looking over a beautiful expanse of water stretching forever, I once had the feeling that I was part of the water. Life is effortless if you are water.

Francie lived in Newport, in an old house that had been split into apartments. I slept on the sofa in her living room, part of which must have once been a sleeping porch. A line of tall windows started in the middle of one wall, then turned the corner and ran all the way down the next wall. One blustery afternoon, the windows rattled in a comforting way, and continued their rattle through the grey, snowy, windy evening, and on into the night. Newport had lots of snow left from the East coast storm of the week before. For our walks during the day, Francie and I made our way single file along the narrow paths cleared from snow on the sidewalks.

On the reverse trip home, I felt such ease when I got back to Penn Station. I knew where the waiting room was, where to buy food. I had learned that train travelers in that station periodically congregate around the huge arrival-departure screen just outside the waiting room. I think train notices were only posted a few minutes before time to arrive or depart, something like that.

Boarding the *Crescent* again was more than just easy. I felt more than confidence. I felt trust. Really. Trust in Amtrak. It's the greatest feeling. I got a window seat again. Lovely. Double-deckers are fun, and seeing the West out the window is gorgeous, but this was my home train. I loved it the best. I had a seatmate, a woman my age, who almost immediately opened a gallon Ziploc bag of home-assembled trail mix and offered me some. I was amazed at the quantity but more so at the composition. It was full of cashews.

"You use the good stuff!" I said in admiration, as I took a handful.

She laughed. "Oh, yes, I use the good stuff," she said, big emphasis on "yes," as if "Who wouldn't?" She had a deep, shoulder-shaking, comforting rumble of a laugh.

Just before we left the station, another woman our age bustled up the aisle with lots of things and identified the empty seat across from us as hers. She introduced herself to the young man in the window seat, "Hi, I'm Jean," sat down, and immediately started talking to all of us. She gave us a happy soliloquy. I was impressed. This was her first train trip, she was from Upstate New York, she had taken another train to get to Penn Station. She, like me, was traveling to Greenville, going to visit a friend. The friend had left her husband a year before and moved to Greenville. "I don't see any reason to leave *my* husband," she told us, in a thoughtful way, as if she'd given it some thought. "I'm going for a month and he's OK with that."

She was all about trains, even though this was her first trip, about how much better they were than flying, better in all kinds of ways.

This assertion proved mildly controversial. Both my seatmate and our diagonal, yet another woman our age, chimed in their disagreement. Jean was undeterred.

I felt no compunction to join in on her side, even though I agreed with her. How luxurious, to sit back at ease and let my arguments be made for me. She reminded me of me on my first trip, relieved and energized to be actually on the train, full of enthusiasm.

Jean's seatmate was a young man with black glasses who looked Middle Eastern and worked on his laptop. Like me, he didn't join in the debate. Once, at a smoke stop, he got up and left, presumably going outside. He hadn't returned when the train left the station. Jean was worried about him, and stopped the attendant when she walked by. The attendant laughed. "If he didn't get back to the train in time, we can't help that!" But soon afterwards he came back. He'd been in the Club Car, he said. Jean told him how she'd worried.

I, myself, was worrying. I was worrying that he didn't like her. Her voice wasn't loud or grating, at least to me, but maybe he didn't like her talking so much. I needn't have worried. He laughed when she told him she'd been afraid he hadn't made it back to the train, and when she ran into problems with her new iPad he helped her. They leaned their heads together. He seemed to enjoy her. She must have gotten her iPad for her trip. In Penn Station she had taken her first video, she told us, of the man who shared her table at the McDonalds. She had recorded his Lou Rawls impression.

She wanted to video her across-the aisle neighbors, us, and as soon as her seatmate helped her with whatever problem she was having, she pointed the camera our way. "Hi, I'm Anna," I said in a peppy way, smiling and waving. My seatmate laughed and waved. "I'm Brenda."

I ate dinner with a friendly couple from eastern North Carolina. They'd been to visit their daughter. They were making the trip by train for the first time. The train was the wife's idea, and the husband had been skeptical but was enjoying it thoroughly. They had horses, it turned out, and the man had designed his own type of halter. He really loved his horses. We talked about horses, about family and music, and about how we liked to get along with people. Then back to my car. The lights were dimmed and everything grew quiet. The station names became more and more familiar. Near morning, the attendant came through to let Jean and me know that we were approaching Greenville. I gathered my things, trying not to disturb my seatmate, trying to be quiet because it was nighttime and stood as the train slowed. Jean was doing the same across the aisle. I had an unreasonable nervousness that I was going to miss my stop. I stepped carefully over my seatmate, put my coat on, pulled my suitcase down and started to follow Jean towards the door. I wanted to be there when the train stopped, so that I could get off in good time, so that the others could board, so that the stop would be an efficient one.

"Goodbye, Anna," I heard from behind me.

I turned.

"Goodbye…" I hesitated. "Brenda?" She nodded. It was the first time we had spoken each other's names. The train stopped.

I said my goodbye as she had said hers, softly, in a nighttime way. I said mine with real feeling because I was ashamed. I appreciated her goodbye to me. As I made my way off the train I thought about staying guilty for not saying it first and about being unsure of her name, but decided to let it go. I just kept the appreciation. Did I say, "Have a nice rest of your trip"? I hope so. Good Brenda. To be with a generous person is the real gift.

I followed Jean down the steps, and she and I said goodbye to each other. Her friend was waiting for her in a car at the front of the station. They started their greetings and I headed into the parking lot, feeling quietly happy, happy to be back, but mostly happy about the family-of-man experience of my neighborhood on the *Crescent*. Nothing dramatic, nothing big; just good, just complete.

Then a strange thing happened. I almost didn't notice it. I had a thought, faraway, soft, but clear and self-assured. It was, "There's more." I knew, somehow and immediately, what it was about. "More" meant status and possessions and money, things like that. I also knew "There's more" was wrong. I let it go. I looked for my car. I suppose that the thought "There's more" was a deep belief of mine. I'm sure it's still there, in with a thousand other beliefs, but maybe, hopefully, it's a little weaker now. It was a strange experience, and I haven't had another one quite like it, not yet.

CHAPTER 31

Home

Back once more to 2011, summer, my first trip, with me in the DC train station, feeling relieved that I was headed south for home. Boarding was called and I got on the *Crescent* for what I thought would be the last time ever. My seatmate Caroline was a college student, bright and friendly, going to Charlotte to visit her sister. We sat near the front of the car. We had front-row seats for the welcome and information talk given by our young showman of an attendant, who gave his show for Caroline. He had a crush on her. So did the quiet young ticket-taker who came along later. It wasn't easy for him to look at her, and he was flustered when asking for her ticket. Caroline was nice to them both, but didn't flirt, didn't let on or maybe didn't know that they thought her pretty. I pulled out my knitting after a while and she watched me knit. I read once of a knitting teacher who travels by train because she is afraid of flying, and packs extra yarn and needles in case a seatmate wants to learn.

Across the aisle from us, taking up two rows, was a young family, parents and two children. It was pleasant to be near them. The children were happy and well-mannered, and the parents had brought things for them to do. I asked Caroline about her parents. Her mother worked for ATF, which I learned was Alcohol, Tobacco and Firearms, a government agency, and her father worked for the railroad. I asked about her school. She was on the gymnastics team, which I thought sounded fun. "They work you hard!" she said. I laughed, and believed her. She was a great girl. It's important to take note of the good things that are happening in America. I found that easy to do on the train.

I ate dinner with another pretty woman, Rosalee, who was traveling to a mid-sized town in the Deep South, in order to move there. She wasn't happy about the move. The company she worked for, a small business, was sending her there. "Catfish?" she said to me, with more than a hint of disapproval. "That's the only kind of fish they have there. What kind of fish is called 'catfish'? It doesn't even sound good."

Rosa had grown up on an island in the Caribbean. Her grandfather had brought home fish almost every day, so many different kinds of fish. She named some when I asked, a long list, and not one of those she named I'd ever heard of. She was moving from New Jersey and she liked her life there. She was particular, asking questions of the waiter about the menu, taking her time to decide what to order, asking for a cup of hot water to accompany the soup she chose, in case the soup was too salty for her taste, which it was. She ate slowly. I, on the other hand, had trouble not eating unmannerly fast because I was hungry and my dinner tasted so good. It was a creation. It was the Pasta Dish, which I hesitated to order because the one other time I'd ordered the Pasta it turned out to be slightly overcooked noodles with an uninteresting sauce. This Dish was perfect. It was lasagna noodles with a mushroom and cream cheese filling, and a tasty tomato sauce over all.

Rosa had traveled once to the Southern town that was to become her new home, and the visit had done nothing to boost her enthusiasm. I asked how much luggage she had brought this time, wondering what I'd bring if I were having to move. Two extra-big suitcases, she said. Filled with clothes? I asked. She was a sharp dresser. One is, she said. And the other? She didn't want to say. "Muffins," she said, finally. Muffins? I smiled. "Yes," she said, serious. "They don't have good muffins there."

Oh, I liked her! She may have fallen in love with her new town. You never know.

Sometime around five a.m., early in the morning of that August day in 2011, seventeen days after I'd left for Seattle, the *Crescent* pulled into the Greenville station. I didn't know if Dee would be there to meet me. I'd told him that it didn't matter, and it truly didn't. Greenville was home. Dee would have to get up at three in the morning to be there when my train arrived. I told him

I'd be fine to wait. I could have stayed at the station or maybe even walked to the McDonald's where we had eaten dinner. I could have passed the time easily until he made it. I only cared about being done with my train trip. But he was there to meet me, and it was lovely to see him.

CHAPTER 32

The Last Chapter

My grandmother grew up outside of Danville, Virginia, a railroad center. In her childhood, during the latter part of the 1800's, wealthy families in that place timed weddings so that the married couple could leave the reception and get on the train. Restless young men took the train, or were put on the train, for the West.

Her daughter, my mother, rode the train from Richmond to El Paso with the little girl who was her first child, the girl who was to be my oldest sister. The two were riding to meet my Dad, who was stationed in El Paso, waiting to be shipped out to Europe for the war. My mother says there were lots of soldiers on the trains. They were in good spirits, she says, and she wondered, with no little fear, what might be ahead for them.

In December of 2017, *National Geographic* published another of Paul Salopek's articles—Salopek, the man who is walking the path of human migration. For this article, he wrote of his walk across Central Asia, across grassland, desert and mountains, and, for a bit, alongside a "steamy river." It took him 199 days. All of this was following the loosely defined route known as the Silk Road.

Beware of the jinn, he was told. Jinn are spirits of the steppes. Most are malevolent.

"What should I do if a jinn harasses me?" Salopek asked a native, wolf hunter Karim Junelbekov.

"No matter what it does, no matter how frightening it is, don't panic or show emotion," answered Junelbekov. "Just sit down on a rock and wait. It will lose interest. It will go away."

Aung San Suu Kyi, the woman who was held under house arrest for fifteen years by the military dictatorship in Myanmar, the woman who pretended to be courageous when she felt afraid, was elected to the newly-formed parliament in 2015. "She is barred from the presidency," says Michael Ignatieff in his 2017 book *The Ordinary Virtues*. Suu Kyi, as elected leader, has come under international criticism for failing to do enough to protect from violence a Muslim minority group in her country. In this book, Ignatieff continues his preferred method of investigation, traveling to the world's troubled spots, this time looking explicitly for "ethics in action," and he writes a chapter on Myanmar and "the Lady," as Suu Kyi is called, including and taking a cautious step beyond the criticism. We meet an anti-Muslim Buddhist monk with a large following, and hear from peace-loving imams of "a radical Islam coming from outside." We are invited to consider problems relevant to a newborn democracy, and problems of misinformation. Ignatieff's new book is gritty but ultimately reassuring, though just barely, because of what he saw on the ground in Myanmar and other places. He saw courage, tenacity, generosity and hospitality. Skip the introduction if it bogs you down, and go straight to the stories. He is a good writer. He makes interesting what I might have been tempted to avoid.

I couldn't shake my guilt over throwing away Alice Munro's book of short stories *Runaway,* so I bought another copy. I re-read the stories I'd read on the trip, "Runaway" and "Powers," the first and the last in the book. I found her writing as exhilarating as I had remembered. The characters in these stories are as close to alive as I think writing can go. You can't know all about them, and you will never exactly figure them out. They will surprise you, but the surprise is credible. Munro's insight into human nature makes me want to read on, discover more, and that insight offers a chance to see humanity with more compassion.

The ending of "Runaway" was easier to take since I'd been there before, and I didn't see it as the hopeless indictment I'd seen the first time. Ominous and ugly, to be sure, but not necessarily hopeless. I could even imagine the story as a mirror for us all, showing how we can make unwise compromises when we are not yet strong. That's OK. It's part of being human. We live and, let's hope, learn.

"Powers" was beautiful. I'd completely missed the spark of rescue at the end. I had pre-judged and I was reading impatiently the first time.

I read the other stories in the collection. Maybe there's a theme. Maybe there's at least one character in each story who goes through and beyond sadness. I'd need to read it again to test that theory. I'll keep it for now. Maybe I will read it again for, at least, the sheer excitement of the writing.

Did Caribbean-born Rosalee ever try catfish? There's a story.

I like catfish, but it doesn't come my way often. I know of people who pass on the slow-maturing ocean fish, out of concern for cost or for the health of oceans, but will eat the fast-growing catfish or tilapia. I eat less meat nowadays. There are so many ways to help.

Not long ago, I had trouble sleeping, and the only thing I could find to calm me as I lay in the dark, was a scene that appeared like the beginning of a dream. I was sitting on the floor, in dim light, with the big goofy White guy, the talker, the "Mon-TAN-N-N-a-a-a" guy, and his across-the-aisle neighbor, the big shy Black man. We each had a plate of salmon and rice. We liked each other. The talker was carrying the conversation, mostly monologuing, and I enjoyed being in the presence of the shy man. Both of them really. It felt like holiness. In the tranquility, I took over as creator, specifying that the salmon was wild-caught, and that stocks were abundant, because of excellent fish management.

In December of 2018, I took the *Crescent* north to Delaware, to spend Christmas with my sister in Wilmington. The train was five hours late leaving Greenville. It had left New Orleans on time, but freight had caused delays. No one in the small, full waiting room had ever remembered it being so late. The Greenville station was, by 2018, unstaffed, and announcements about changing departure times were made at intervals during the night over the intercom. We finally boarded at 4 a.m.

I didn't mind the wait. I was able to nap by making a tower of my suitcase on end, my daypack, and my soft pocketbook, and then laying my head on my pocketbook. I felt a warm affection for the people waiting with me. I listened to talk, and the voices were music.

"When we were kids," said a man my age talking with a woman my age, "my mama would make cakes and pies for Christmas and she would keep them in what we called a 'pie safe.' We'd come into the house from playing and we didn't go over and cut ourselves a slice of cake. No sir. Nobody sliced the cake but Mama. If you came in from playing, and there were slices on the table, that's when you'd have your cake."

The woman laughed, and those of us who were listening smiled. This was familiar.

I had my own seat all the way to Wilmington. I saw a few wrapped Christmas packages among people's things. If I was walking through a car and passed someone from the Greenville waiting room, we'd smile and nod to each other.

My sister lived then in a house with four working-age young people, one woman and three men. One of the young men cleared the dining room table of the piles of scrapbooks and books and papers that had resided there since my sister's husband died, three years previously. Then the young man cleaned and polished the table. We ate all our dinners there. My sister cooks less and less as the years pass, but she will always be my favorite cook.

The young woman of the group constructed the house Christmas tree. She strung white lights in a zig-zag tree design on a bare wall over a sofa in the den. Hung in the lights were colorful ornaments, many from Mexico. After a dinner of Greek spaghetti on Christmas Eve, some of us went to the service at my sister's church. Christmas dinner was Carnitas, the Mexican pork dish. Relaxed and festive was that holiday in Wilmington.

I shared a seat with a large man coming back, which was fine. He was a nice man, and I've gotten better at sleeping in odd positions and in not stressing if I don't sleep. I had great dining companions, both going up and returning home.

Pillows weren't handed out. I don't think the lights were dimmed as much at night. The food was not as good as it had been and there were fewer choices. They probably wouldn't put you up in a hotel anymore, although I did see insurance offered in case of delays. My political cousin says that Amtrak has cut services. Still, the trip was wonderful for me.

Something had changed for me personally. I felt joy, before, during, and after this ride. I felt like I belonged on the train, that I was one of them, one of the regulars.

"Amtrak was never designed to be anything more than an exit strategy from the rail industry's deficits," says F.K.Plous, in the trade journal *Railway Age*.

"The Amtrak era is over. It's time for a replacement" is the title of his article.

Referencing Rush Loving's "magisterial" book *The Men Who Loved Trains,* Plous describes the situation surrounding the beginning of Amtrak. "President Nixon agreed to sign the 1970s Railpax legislation that created Amtrak only because the congressional aides who drafted it persuaded him that Amtrak would last only about five years." People were going to drive or fly.

When that didn't happen, when "Americans started riding the trains again–and demanding more trains, Amtrak didn't know what to do…And it still doesn't…"

Plous argues, competently and persuasively, that national passenger train service decisions can only be made "by the establishment of a new National Transportation Policy that positions passenger train development at the same level of importance as highways and civil aviation." It won't be easy, he says, but he reminds us that neither highways nor air traffic were initially considered to be federal responsibilities.

My friend David, in my writing group, is the first person I told, after Dee, about my idea of making a book. When I told him, I found out that he himself had taken a trip on the Greenville train. He rode to Washington, DC with his son's 5th grade class, "when Jimmy Carter was president." David called it "the night train." I liked that. It made me think of some of those train songs.

David is a world traveler, and also a published author. He is kind. He is a good listener, and makes you feel safe. He is also a careful thinker, and he says thoughtful things.

It was a huge step for me to tell anyone about my idea of writing, because creating a book seemed, at the beginning, almost impossibly scary.

"People in our country don't ride trains too much." I said that to David to try to explain why I would write on this subject, knowing that he, world traveler, understood what passenger trains mean in other parts of the world. I think I picked the right person to tell.

"No," he said, in his calm, easy way, "they don't." He was quiet for what seemed like a long time. I knew he was thinking.

"But they used to," he said.

Anna Raglan
December, 2019

Made in United States
Troutdale, OR
01/29/2024

17264945R00139